THE

Bouncebackability

FACTOR

END BURNOUT, GAIN RESILIENCE,
CHANGE THE WORLD

By

Caitlin Donovan

Dedication

For my grandmothers, whose emotions I carry in my DNA and on whose shoulders I stand.

CONTENTS

INTRODUCTION

WHY WRITE THIS BOOK?

The simple explanation for writing this book is because I needed it, and no one else wrote it for me. This book has been a long time in the making and is the sum of years and years of experience with patients, clients, and mostly, myself. I didn't know for a long time that burnout is what I was treating in my acupuncture clinic (or feeling in myself) because it came to me disguised in: fertility issues, migraines, fatigue, and other chronic health problems. In fact, had you told me I was burnt out while it was happening, I would have scoffed and said you were crazy.

It took my own burnout, before I turned 30, for recognition of this pattern to start to take hold. I found myself hating a job I loved, and resenting patients and clients because they needed me. I knew my choices were making me exhausted, but I didn't understand how I could choose differently. My ability to bounce back was a 0/10. So, I did the smartest thing I could think of – I ran away. My husband and I moved to a different country and I started the cycle all over. Three years later, when I started having the same feelings again, I woke up and realized that I couldn't keep running from this. That sooner or later, no matter where I was, this pattern was going to repeat unless I paid attention.

Even with all my knowledge in the worlds of alternative medicine and spirituality, it took me another three years before I figured out what was really going on. I was burning myself out and destroying my own ability to recover from it in the process over and over, without even noticing. I thought I was getting cranky with age. I blamed my diet. I blamed the people I worked with. I blamed anything I could, when the majority of the answers, as per usual, were within.

As a healthcare practitioner who owned her own business, I was setting myself up for burnout every time and not doing what I needed to do to be able to bounce back. It wasn't the structure of my business that was burning me out and crushing my internal stress management abilities. It wasn't the amount of money I was making. It was a combination of: my driving force, my definition of success, my inability to be honest about my stress levels, my environment, and my rooted-in-trauma people-pleasing tendencies.

These tendencies were a coping mechanism that I created earlier in my life and they meant that I would give patients more than they were asking for in terms of time and energy. I found myself working before my opening hours, through lunch, and after closing – all the while explaining that I *never* do this so they should be extra appreciative. (They never were, of course, and it wasn't really their job to be!) My definition of success was: help as many people as possible and make as much money as possible. So, I said 'yes' too many times when I wanted to say no. I was more invested in my patients' results than they were, so I was doing extra research, going to week-long courses instead of taking vacations and constantly feeling like none of it was enough.

Entrepreneurial burnout is a beast and it was killing me. My motivation for getting shit done was stuck in 'prove myself' mode. My drive forward was: "How can I make the money I need for X?" In the back of my mind, I thought that if I just built this business, I'd prove I was valuable. If I gave myself up for my patients, they would

2

know I was worthy. If I made enough money, I'd finally prove that I had *made it* out of the city I grew up in. And then people would *know* I had made it. And me? Well, I couldn't be that stressed. I was an expert in stress management; obviously, it couldn't happen to *me*!

None of these were conscious thoughts and I didn't recognize them until after the second time I burnt out. Even as I write them now, my response to myself is: "Relax kid, those are ridiculous things to say!" Yet still, deep down, I know that my motivation had been to prove my worthiness, and hide from my internal pain and suffering. To all intents and purposes, on the surface, I did just that. From the outside, I had proved it. I built successful businesses in two different countries and languages. I was teaching on an international stage (in a foreign language) before my 30th birthday. My patients and students and course participants loved me (for the most part) and I even had a friend tell me that I had (and I quote) "everything that everyone wants."

My life looked good on the outside. It was impressive, yes. But there was a storm brewing under the surface that I'd helped other people through but hadn't weathered myself. I knew that long-term stress could cause health problems. I mean, hell, that fact was the very basis of my day-to-day work with patients. That was what I was working with every day. What I didn't realize was that I could be chronically stressed without even knowing it. It's the insidious stress that gets us the worst. The stress you brush away thinking, *that can't possibly be bothering me, it was five years ago, I'm totally over it*, or *that didn't even bother me, I'm fine with it*. Bullshit. My body wasn't over it no matter how much justification was happening in my head.

When I started looking around for help, I wasn't sure where to turn. At that time, there was no such thing as a burnout coach. With the help of friends, family, coaches, functional medicine, and

3

Chinese medicine, I bounced my way back. I'm big on researching and reading everything available on a subject, but with burnout, I ran into a problem: nearly all burnout research and books had a focus on the workplace. At the time, I even had access to academic research and everything I found was about corporations, hospitals, and offices. This problem increased when in June 2019 the World Health Organization dubbed burnout an 'occupational hazard'. More articles became available, but none of them were about *me* and my situation.

What are those of us with our own businesses supposed to do? We don't have to change the corporate status quo, but we do need to change both the rampant burnout culture that surrounds us and our own internal world that puts us on a burnout path. Burnout, you'll hear me say over and over, is a combination of internal and external factors. As an entrepreneur, you're responsible for both of those. My hope for this book is that it helps you find your way through burnout faster and more easily than I did and increases your bouncebackability factor so much that, no matter what happens, you hold an unshakeable belief: with the right support, the willingness to really see yourself, and the choice to heal, you will *always* be able to bounce back from burnout.

WHO SHOULD READ THE BOUNCEBACKABILITY FACTOR?

Chronic stress is building up and burning you out. It's the stress based on the way you view yourself and the world. The stress created when the world appears to be different from the pictures of it that you imagined in your mind. It's the tension that arises when following your own rule book doesn't lead you to the pot of gold that you were told it would. The tension that comes from overstepping your own internal boundaries because you're a 'nice person'. This shit piles up, people.

When it was happening to me, I got more curious about the processes that accompany long-term stress and I stumbled upon an article that informed me our frontal cortex (the part of the brain responsible for logical thinking) is shrinking because of chronic stress. In addition, the center of the brain responsible for stress management shrinks. This leaves you with the inability to deal with stress as it comes. So, not only are you not handling old stress well, but there's no way you'll be able to handle new stress either because your brain is no longer well equipped to deal!

I thought about that for months and months. I wrote a few blog posts. I did more research. It turns out your brain really does change shape and size with chronic stress. When your frontal cortex shrinks, your limbic system takes over. (Alini, 2017)

In layman's terms, you start to be controlled by your emotions and impulses − by your unexamined rule book that you were 'gifted' as a child, by the patterns and beliefs you inherited from the generations before you, and by the ways of being that society tells you are correct. You get caught up in a tornado where it doesn't feel like you have any control or influence over your life. But we know, as entrepreneurs, that not only is that not true, but we opened our businesses because that's not how we function! Nearly every womxn entrepreneur I've ever met works for herself because she didn't accept all the standard ways of doing things. She had an idea, a feeling, a nudge that doing it differently and on her own terms would make it better. However, as the adage goes, wherever you go, there you are. As we wiggle out of societal expectations to create something new, the unexamined beliefs and systems we carry come with us for the journey and cause us to crash.

You have outbursts, you cannot handle difficult situations, you make rash decisions, you eat whatever you are craving without thought to consequences because your brain and body *demand* it. You've lost control and gaining it back feels impossible. You're exhausted all day but all the switches turn on at night making it impossible to sleep. You've built a successful business but you daydream about your car sliding off the road – maybe you die, maybe you don't – either way you get a break, right? You entered the entrepreneurial world and built a passion-based business. You help people! You're good! So, why don't you feel good?

The good news is that it isn't impossible to recover, you can sleep restfully again and you can gain back health and control after burnout. A simple vacation won't do it. Neither will a massage. Running away gives reprieve but it is short-lived. It takes more than that to recover from burnout. And in this book, I'm going to share all the best research along with all my favorite tricks and tips for recovery and prevention of burnout.

Nothing that I will write in this book is groundbreaking, nor is it meant to be. This book is being written to reach an audience that hasn't found this topic yet because no one wrote it to them. There are burnout books for doctors and nurses, for mothers, and for high-level professionals. I haven't found one yet for passionate womxn entrepreneurs, like myself, that made me feel seen and heard. I'm hoping that you find yourself in this book and that you're able to apply these principles to help yourself back away from burnout.

WHO THE HECK AM I ANYWAY?

Before we get too deep into it, I'll take a second to introduce myself. My name is Caitlin Donovan and I am...

They say the words that follow 'I am' are the most powerful words in your vocabulary. My natural tendency here, especially as author of this book, is to write about the parts that will impress you. My degree, my accomplishments, my blue ribbons would be the things I would say first. But I'm going to flip that on its head. I want you to know what kind of human I am before you find out what kind of schooling I did and why I'm qualified to write this book.

My name is Caitlin Donovan and I am a highly sensitive person with a tendency toward anxiety, covered in a tough shell of Massachusetts brashness for protection. I love to laugh and to make people laugh. I get full body chills when I feel that something that was said is really *true*. I have mediumship abilities that I never took the time to expand upon or learn more about. I come from two incredibly strong ancestral lines that I feel coursing through my body every day.

For most of my life, my biggest pride was book smarts. I was a nerd in school. I loved all things science and getting perfect grades. I left high school assuming I'd be an MD someday. An amazing professor and a love for all things Eastern led me to a Master's degree in Chinese Medicine instead. I have always loved living on the edge of what's considered 'normal'. I've always had different and creative friends who I cherish more than they'll every probably truly understand. I like things that are different. I like to live a life that makes good stories.

Most of my growth has come from reading and travel. I have spent well over a decade of my life in foreign countries. I am a polyglot and speak both Polish and English at home with my Polish husband, Marcin. My parents and sister are my true North, and my ability to travel and live abroad was built on the foundation that they created. I always knew exactly where home was, no matter where I was in the world physically.

My biggest flaws are my big mouth, my sugar addiction (feel free to send chocolate if you loved this book), and my uber independence, which can make people feel disconnected from me sometimes. I like being with a book and a mug of something warm (but not hot) more than… well, almost anything. I spend most of my money on Kindle books and love a good pencil skirt and sneaker combo.

My burnout happened while I was doing a job I loved and that was so confusing for me. I followed the rules of finding the thing that makes you happy and doing it. I even did it successfully. I helped hundreds of couples have babies in the first six years of my life as a fertility acupuncturist. I made enough money to cover my bills, my student loans, and nearly any vacation that I wanted. I married my perfect person. What life could be more rewarding or satisfying?

I sure as shit didn't know the answer to that question. I was disappointed with adulting, especially because I did all the right things.

While I was in Poland, just after grad school, I met Ewa Blaszczak, life coach extraordinaire, and we started a fertility coaching business while I apprenticed with her. We had so much fun but fertility had never really been the right fit for me. In the end, I learned the life coaching skills and Ewa and I let the initial excitement for our business fizzle.

So, here I was, gathering all the skills that I would use, 10 years later, to get myself out of burnout. I just didn't know it at the time. Instead, I kept plugging on, as one does, ignoring the stress I was facing – in denial about it really.

All these things together, plus my experience of burning out twice, make me the best person to write this exact book right now. I've taken in the information, I've read the books and embodied the wisdom. I've traveled to China to do weeks of self-cultivation. I've transformed my life little by little. My skills in Chinese medicine and life coaching combined create the perfect backdrop to support you on a burnout journey. It also helps that I'm dying to tell you about it and dying to help you change that path. If you've found yourself following the rules and ending up disappointed and disconnected from your passion, this book is for you.

PART ONE

BURNING OUT

CHAPTER 1

WHAT IS BURNOUT?

The term 'burnout' was coined in the 1970s by the American psychologist Herbert Freudenberger. He used it to describe the consequences of severe stress and high ideals in 'helping' professions. Doctors and nurses, for example, who sacrifice themselves for others, would often end up being 'burned out' – exhausted, listless, and unable to cope. Nowadays, the term is not only used for these helping professions, or for the dark side of self-sacrifice. It seems it can affect anyone, from stressed-out careerists and celebrities to overworked employees and homemakers.

Surprisingly, there is no clear definition of what burnout really is. As a result, it's not clear what burnout is exactly or how we can identify it. This also makes it impossible to say how common it is.

The lack of a clear definition for burnout has been a point of contention for burnout researcher Christina Maslach as she explained in the book *Burnout: The Cost of Caring*. As she reviews the existing literature, she noted that, "What was meant by the term 'burnout' varied widely from one writer to the next. As a result, these writers were sometimes talking about different phenomena rather than the same one." Not only was there a discrepancy in the definitions, but the concept of burnout was expanded to encompass such an unhelpful range of problems as to end up being meaningless. According to Maslach, "Almost every personal problem that one can think of was described as 'burnout' at some point." (Christina Maslach, 1982)

Maslach and her team eventually created a 22 question survey to 'diagnose' burnout and it is known as the Maslach Burnout Inventory. According to her research, burnout has three aspects: 1. Physical and emotional exhaustion, 2. Poor performance and feeling unaccomplished, and 3. Cynicism and detachment. This is now the most widely used 'definition' of burnout, but it's hardly complete. As Maslach said herself in a 2018 interview on *Radio Times*, "[Burnout] is not just symptoms in the sense of a disease, it really is an experience that people are having, and so the characteristics of that experience are 1. Stress – you're getting the kind of exhaustion that comes from feeling stressed about work but with burnout we also see... a sense in which people are getting very negative about the job... they don't do as good a job, they don't treat people as well, and they can also eventually have a negative evaluation of themselves." (Maslach, Lee, & Neason, 2018)

So, if we can't just list a set of symptoms, let me describe the experience for you as an amalgamation of my own experience plus the experiences of hundreds of my patients and clients.

Burnout is a state of being that affects physical, emotional, and mental wellbeing. It is the extreme that occurs when stress is chronic enough to cause changes to the structure of the brain, your ability to digest, your heart rate and more, making you less able to handle further stress and more inclined to severe physical and emotional symptoms that are a result of said stress. In super simple terms, burnout is the result of chronic stress that changes your ability to handle day-to-day life with ease.

Stress, in and of itself, isn't the problem. Your body has these amazing regulatory systems to keep your body constantly in a place of homeostasis. Homeostasis is your body's ability to keep everything balanced. For instance, when bacteria is present and could cause a cold, your immune system reacts and kills the bacteria, thereby maintaining balance. When it's hot outside, you sweat to cool down. Anything that causes your body to react in order to maintain balance is referred to as stress. Small bouts of stress here and there are fine. Your body and mind adjust, and you move on. It's the chronic stress that continues and continues, the stress we mostly deny or ignore, that gets us in the end. When the body's natural ability to maintain homeostasis is hampered by the sheer amount of work it needs to do, it starts to break down. It focuses on the easiest things, the most important things. Your body, like your life, has a to-do list that it just can't keep up with. In each person, the physical and emotional symptoms will be different based on their natural tendencies, their previous sicknesses or injuries, and their current situation.

For example, Suzy comes in for an acupuncture treatment and complains that she's having headaches. When asked about her stress levels, she says, "Normal," and doesn't expand upon that answer. Just looking at her, it's obvious that her shoulders are tight and her jaw is clenched. We go through her history and it turns out that she was in a car accident and had whiplash 12 years prior. That's where the headaches began, but they aren't consistent, so she doesn't see a pattern. For Suzy, because of her previous whiplash, it's likely that stress-related symptoms will show up in her head and neck. The body remembers traumas and uses them as the easiest and quickest possible signal to let you know that something is off. If there is a weakness somewhere, that's what the body will use to set off the alarm. Headaches, in Suzy's case, are the first sign of chronic stress leading to burnout.

In my life, the first thing that happens is overwhelming anxiety. If someone had told me years ago that I was an anxious person, I would have scoffed, but the truth remains that I am and always have been. My anxiety is rooted in traumas during childhood related to abandonment. When I begin to feel anxious and overwhelmed and start to do everything too quickly and feel like I'm never going to catch up and thus no one will love me because I won't be productive, that's a sign that I haven't been paying attention to myself very well and burnout is tapping me on the shoulder.

In your life, it could be depression, insomnia, IBS, a flare-up of colitis, asthma, panic attacks, anxiety, heart palpitations, irritability, skin breakouts, pretty much anything which gets worse with stress, which is… everything. So, in addition to the three components that Christina Maslach found in her research (exhaustion, negativity, and poor performance), there is likely a sign (or five) of your burnout which is yours and yours alone. When you find out what your particular symptom is, you can use it as a guiding tool to help you stay on track and prevent burnout. Your sign or signs can be mental, emotional, physical or spiritual or a combo deal, if that's how you roll. I'll help you find it in this book. (You might even have a few ideas what yours are after reading these few paragraphs!)

There's another question that remains unanswered in the research: is burnout a result of your outside environment, or your personality and ability to deal with stress? I will talk about this in-depth later, but for now, allow me to share with you a bit about my own first burnout in hope of shedding light on how I feel personally about this topic.

At the age of 24, I moved from sunny San Diego, California to Warsaw, Poland. I made such a drastic move as soon as I finished my Master's degree in order to be with the man I loved. It was bold and it would cost me (and teach me) more than I ever thought possible. As a couple, we spent six years in Warsaw and had a good degree of success. I managed to learn Polish fluently, create a position in a fertility clinic as the first person in the country to do so, and then follow that up with opening a private practice that had me seeing over 60 patients a week with a three-month waiting list.

I was the girl who 'did it all'. By all outside measures, I was a huge success. I was paying off my ginormous student loans far faster than my American counterparts even though I was underearning them per treatment by approximately 60%, the price of treatments in Poland and the exchange rate both affected this. All of this action would be enough to burn someone out, and while this was a part of my burnout, the larger part was the environment I was in.

Poland is a difficult country for an expat, but if you listen to her citizens, they'll tell you much the same. There is an underlying need to fight, a lot of aggression and passive aggression, you need to be able to stand your ground at all times to thrive there. The country's history is riddled with wars, strong judgmental Catholicism seeps into every part of daily life, and methods of figuring things out left over from Communist times were completely foreign to me. Daily, I would get phone calls from women seeking to have acupuncture with me. My schedule was constantly full and I *knew* exactly when the next available slots were – in three months' time. I know being put on a waiting list wasn't what people wanted, but I was stretched to my gills.

This is how the conversation usually went:

Patient: "Hello, I'd like to make an appointment."

Me: "Okay, great. I can offer you [date three months from now]. If you don't want to wait that long, you can see a colleague of mine who now works in the fertility clinic that I started in. She is available this week."

Patient: "Why don't you check again?"

Me: "I know my schedule. I know this is the time I have available."

Patient: "You should take a look at this week's schedule and try to fit me in."

Me: "I'm sorry, that's not possible. I'm completely full."

Patient: "Well, then, you *could* take me by coming in early, staying late, or treating me during your lunch hour."

Me: "I'm sorry, that's not possible. I'm completely full this week. If you'd like an appointment with me, one is available on [date]. If you don't want to wait, you can see my colleague."

Patient: "Are you sure?"

And on and on it went. It got to the point where I was afraid to answer my phone if it was an unknown number because I didn't want to go through this amazing boundary-pushing exercise yet again. The Poles are amazing boundary-pushers. Often, it is what they need to do to get things done. This works with other doctors and professionals. I just didn't know how to function with that much pressure, nor how to hold boundaries in a way that protected me and was still kind. I even had one particular phone call at 7:00 am on a Saturday that ended in a woman screaming at me for being irresponsible for having a website if I'm not taking new patients immediately. I hung up. But I was shaken up about it for the next few days. I got into my profession because I wanted to help people but the demand for my help was more than I could handle.

During this time, my friend Ewa and I discussed this phenomenon often, and as is usual in the world of personal development, we focused on all the things I could do to change my mindset. I changed and I changed and I changed. I practiced meditative techniques, I started a gratitude journal, I practiced Metta (loving-kindness) when I was out and about in the city. But whatever I did, I didn't feel better. My daily interactions with people were still sour. The environment just wasn't working for me. The energy of Warsaw and the energy of Cait just weren't resonating.

If you have a flower that isn't blooming even after watering and adjusting the sunlight, you change its soil. That was what was necessary for me that time around. I am convinced that *much* of our predisposition to burnout is internal, but you cannot ignore your environment. If you need to be replanted, you need to be replanted – whether that be into a new country, city, job, or relationship. No amount of inner work or affirmations will make you feel good in an environment, job, or relationship that doesn't work for you. There is only so much influence you have over your environment.

During my first burnout, I wanted to believe that if I meditated and loved Polish people enough, I could have a better experience. I wanted to have more control. I wanted what I was doing to be enough to create comfort for myself, but that wasn't possible. There are centuries of traumas and ways of doing things embedded into the people and the culture of Poland that my meditations weren't about to flip around. I felt tricked by The Secret, The Law of Attraction and all those spiritual practices that kept telling me that I controlled everything, that I created my surroundings. It felt like I was failing at being spiritual and kind.

This is the tricky part of entrepreneurial burnout – you *are* creating a lot of your environment. In a recent interview on *Radio Times*, Kirsten Lee, a behavioral science expert at Northeastern University told us that when the World Health Organization named burnout as an occupational hazard, they also shared information that, "By the year 2030 stress-related illness is going to surpass communicable disease, so we're seeing the data suggest this worldwide epidemic and they're actually calling today's work environments 'modern hazards'." (Maslach, Lee, & Neason, 2018) One of the answers that I want to give you in this book is to the question: what do you do if you've created your own modern hazard?

There have been studies that show Type A personalities (raising hand emoji) have a higher predisposition to burnout, as do women (double whammy over here). There are theories that guess why women have a higher predisposition, but I'll offer the most obvious explanation: we do more and earn less. Often, part of the reason we set up home-based businesses is to be more available to family. However, we fail to make great boundaries between working time and family time. Our businesses feel like side hustles even when we are the main breadwinners or when our businesses take up the same amount of time (if not more) as a full-time job.

I am not a mother myself, but in the world of women entrepreneurs, many are. It seems that when men start businesses, women pick up all the slack in the home to help out. When women start businesses? It is *still* up to them to start their business and run the business of their home without added support. In fact, in the book *High Octane Women: How Superachievers Can Avoid Burnout*, author Dr. Sherrie Bourg Carter refers to a study by Ann Hewlett that tells us: "Unlike men who hold extreme jobs, women are much less likely to have the support of an at-home spouse... The number of men with an at-home spouse is more than double that of women who have this luxury" (Bourg Carter, 2010). It's a recipe for burnout and no one is talking about it. They're all too busy posting pictures on Instagram of their white desks with just a laptop on them to discuss the pile of laundry and dirty dishes we are all dealing with in the background. This never-ending to-do list is enough to send people over the edge.

Chronic, unprocessed and undealt with stress leads to burnout. Environments that constantly add stress through lack of autonomy, micromanaging, lack of recognition and never-ending to-do lists break down your ability to deal with stress. Chronic, unprocessed and undealt with stress also changes your brain structure and multiple other functions in your body from your gut to your immunity. It has long been known that the body and brain work together and that stress can cause physiological changes in the body. It is generally accepted that stress can be a cause of disease. What is not discussed is the fact that when you've been carrying stress around long enough, it is more difficult to recover because your ability to respond appropriately to stress is diminished.

In reading this book, my hope is that you recognize what holds you in patterns of behavior that lead you down that path, and then use the exercises herein to help you recover and even make friends with burnout. Burnout will become your guidepost. It will peek its head out when it's time for you to dig deeper, to uncover another layer, to shift even closer to your authentic self. In addition, as you notice the guidance that your burnout is giving you, you'll build resilience, which I call bouncebackability. Bouncebackability will forever reduce your fear around burnout and allow you to feel empowered when it rears its head.

CHAPTER 2

WHAT DOES BURNOUT FEEL LIKE? (AND HOW DOES IT DIFFER FROM DEPRESSION?)

"I honestly wished I could drive off the road into a tree. At least then, if I survived, I'd have a break. And if I didn't, it would be over."

This statement is a version of what a few different women have told me when I've spoken to them over the years. Burnout is *this* bad. Bad enough to want a car accident. Bad enough to wish for death. Bad enough to be relieved that you've ended up in the hospital, because at least other people can care for you for a while and you get a break. When you're in the middle of a high-stress life, it literally seems impossible that anything could ever be different. Everything is pointless and you feel like a loser who got this far in life by not doing anything of value. It doesn't matter what your job is. It doesn't matter if you have kids. It doesn't matter if the things you've done so far have saved entire countries or fed entire cities. You do not feel any positive impact that your life has had – and other people telling you that you've been impactful doesn't change that.

By the time I was deep into burnout #1, I had helped hundreds of couples have babies that they so desperately wanted. I was helping people to *create lives* and being praised on a *daily basis*. I was still happy for my patients and their partners. I saw and felt their joy... For them. For me? It did nothing. I feel guilty even writing that. What kind of person doesn't understand the value in that kind of work? I'll tell you what kind: the burnt-out kind.

As mentioned earlier, burnout, by current definition, feels like:

1. Physical and emotional exhaustion

2. Cynicism and detachment

3. Feeling unaccomplished, not impactful

But what does that mean in real life?

Let me share with you the story of Jean, a fictional burnt-out woman composed of a few different typical clients to demonstrate burnout while still protecting client privacy.

Jean called me, and it started out pretty typically:

"I'm not sure why I booked this call. I mean I'm tired, but isn't everybody? I'm not even sure it can change, but is this what life should feel like? Is this it?"

And continued:

"I just mostly feel like I wish I could drive off and never come back. I mean, they wouldn't miss me, would they? I fantasize about driving off the road sometimes, hoping that I'd die in the crash, but even if I didn't, then at least I'd create some major change."

And on:

"I mean, I don't want to die, not really. I just imagine it sometimes because it feels like the only way to get out of this. Even dreams of disappearing into the sunset are disrupted by the thought that my family would eventually find me with all their needs waiting in laundry baskets and empty plates."

And more:

"I thought I was doing the right thing, starting this business. I mean, technically, I work in something I love, but I feel so resentful when my clients need things from me. It's like... don't they know how tired I am? I have no bandwidth for any of this."

And when I asked her to describe a typical day she said:

"When I get up, I'm already tired. I get out of bed wondering how I'm going to get through another day and then I just start crossing stuff off the list. None of it feels feasible or possible. And sometimes, I just don't do any of it because I just can't. When my friends call or text, I'm annoyed because I don't have the time to talk to them and it feels like they want to be around me more than I can handle. I don't understand how people love girls' night out – it's so exhausting, I can barely handle my own life, never mind all their complaining. I'm foggy-headed and forget things, and I feel like I'm in the same room as my family but not connected to them. I wish I had an invisible cloak so that I could disappear. By the time I go to bed, I'm still exhausted, but my brain has started going and I have a hard time falling asleep and I'm already overwhelmed thinking about how I have to do it all again tomorrow."

The research is correct. Burnt out people are physically and emotionally exhausted. It's like if your body had two different batteries, one for movement and action, another for thinking and feeling, and both of them were on the fritz. That means that every motion you make is like moving through wet cement, and every thought or feeling is done through a haze. It's all happening, but it doesn't feel real, important or engaging. And in a cruel twist of fate, your brain's battery keeps sparking, so it feels like it's overworking but you can't follow its logic. It sends 102938874938 messages a second and you can't seem to keep up. You're overwhelmed by a brain that you can't keep up with because it's malfunctioning.

Burnt-out people are also cynical and detached. The inner voice becomes Negative Nancy and that bitch dies hard. All of us have a voice that sometimes doesn't sound so great, but when we're burnt out, she's downright nasty. She tells us that nothing we do is valuable, that the world can't change, that no one cares about us unless we're providing something for them. She even finds information in our worlds to back this up. She searches for proof and makes sure we notice it. Her stand becomes everything we believe until the only thought left is: This is all pointless.

Burnt-out people, because of being exhausted and detached, have no ability to see or acknowledge the impact they make on the world, so they fail to see their accomplishments. The tricky thing about burnout is: once you're burnt out, the things you need to do to recover are things that you don't believe in anymore. That's why I feel it's so crucial to have a coach, mentor, or therapist to help you through. You need to borrow someone's eyes and ears until yours are functioning again. Your self-worth and self-belief got shot to hell in a handbasket and someone else needs to help you retrieve them.

The grey cloud of burnout covers everything. It's like the flavor gets removed from life and replaced with a load of stuff that is slightly soured. You can't see a way out clearly. You believe that this is all there is. Your emotions are so far out of regulation that you're snapping at stuff that wouldn't normally bother you and your relationships are suffering. The World Health Organization calls burnout an occupational hazard, but it's an overall wellness hazard. It literally affects everything.

To recap, the symptoms of burnout according to Maslach's Burnout Inventory and the World Health Organization:

1. Emotional and physical exhaustion

2. Low performance/lack of accomplishment

3. Cynicism/depression

In my opinion, we need to add to this list:

- Severe overwhelm

- Resentment

- Tired but wired – exhausted all day with the inability to sleep

- Lack of interest

- Desire to run away and leave it all behind – even if it means death

- Frustration and impatience

- Fatigue

- Being judgmental of self and others

- Neck and shoulder tension

- Explosive emotions

- Feeling depleted

- Suicidal ideation*

- Muscle aches and pains

- Poor digestion

- Cloudy/heavy head

- Negative self-talk

*So many of my podcast guests and clients have told me about their suicidal ideation. Most of these are fantasies, not actual plans with intent to act. That being said, with suicidal ideations or plans, it is crucial that you speak to someone and get support. You can reach out to the Suicide Prevention Hotline, no matter where you live by going here: www.suicidepreventionhotline.org

Just for a kick, let me add the symptoms of depression according to the DSM5 (the book that tells us how to diagnose mental disorders). In order to be diagnosed as having depression, you must exhibit five or more of the following symptoms:

1. Depressed mood most of the day, nearly every day, as indicated by either subjective report (e.g., feeling sad, blue, 'down in the dumps,' or empty) or observations made by others (e.g., appears tearful or about to cry). In children and adolescents, this may present as an irritable or cranky, rather than sad, mood.

2. Markedly diminished interest or pleasure in all, or almost all, activities every day, such as no interest in hobbies, sports, or other things the person used to enjoy doing.

3. Significant weight loss when not dieting or weight gain (e.g. change of more than 5% of body weight in a month), or decrease or increase in appetite nearly every day.

4. Insomnia (inability to get to sleep or difficulty staying asleep) or hypersomnia (sleeping too much) nearly every day.

5. More days than not, problems with sitting still, including constant restlessness, pacing, or picking at one's clothes (called psychomotor agitation by professionals); or the opposite, a slowing of one's movements, talking very quietly with slowed speech (called psychomotor retardation by professionals).

6. Fatigue, tiredness, or loss of energy nearly every day — even the smallest tasks, like dressing or washing, seem difficult to do and take longer than usual.

7. Feelings of worthlessness or excessive or inappropriate guilt nearly every day (e.g., ruminating over minor past failings).

8. Diminished ability to think or concentrate, or indecisiveness, nearly every day (e.g., appears easily distracted, complains of memory difficulties).

9. Recurrent thoughts of death (not just fear of dying), recurrent suicidal ideas without a specific plan, or a suicide attempt or a specific plan for committing suicide.

As you can see, burnout looks a lot like depression according to these definitions, so how do we differentiate the two?

The standard test for burnout, created by Maslach, a psychologist at the University of California, Berkeley, is called the Maslach Burnout Inventory. Over 90% of the research done on burnout uses the Maslach Burnout Inventory, which states that the symptoms of burnout come in a group of three and include: exhaustion, cynicism, and inefficacy. Maslach herself admits that burnout and depression look very similar.

In the work done so far, the biggest delineator that psychologists and researchers use is burnout's direct relation to work or job-related stress. Burnout was originally used to describe what happened to physicians and nurses, i.e., those in highly responsible caretaking roles. It has spread to cover any job-related exhaustion and includes home-related work as well. (Patz, 2015)

In her book *The Joy Of Burnout*, Dina Glouberman tells us: "My view is that one of the major differences between depression and burnout is that depression has to do with failure and loss, while burnout has more to do with a profound disappointment in love, meaning, and our ability to be of service." (Glouberman, 2007)

My view is that burnout and depression are different results with similar causes. I believe that untreated burnout can lead to depression. So, burnout can be part of the road to depression, but doesn't need to be.

My experience of the main difference is that people who are burnt out know they are burnt out and that it's because of overwhelm and too much stress. They also have an inability to rest. It often presents as that 'tired but wired' feeling. You know you can't focus well and things aren't getting done well, but you just can't stop. When you sit to rest, you feel awful and guilty. With depression, on the other hand, it is often hard for the person experiencing it to pinpoint the causes. Sometimes, we hear depression described as 'descending like a cloud' for example.

From the neuroscience research behind chronic stress, it seems that there are certain personality types that lean toward one or the other result so burnout and depression might simply be two sides of the same coin.

Personally, I experienced depression for the first time about two months after rupturing my Achilles tendon. The difference between the times I was burnt out and my experience with depression was this: with depression, you just have to lie down. You may know that things need to get done, but it doesn't seem to matter because there's a stronger apathy than that which happens with burnout. When I've been burnt out, I had to force myself to stop doing things in order to prioritize and redirect my energy. When I was depressed, I just felt like a lump and didn't care what, if anything, got done. When I was burnt out, I could still be in a good mood when I was with people I loved. When depressed, my mood just stayed grey, no matter how great the people around me were.

When I polled my clients and patients for their best descriptions of burnout, here's a cross-section of what they all said:

"Burnout to me is when I am fully drained, not filled up."

"It's like being unmotivated all the time. Even resting feels like a thing you have to do."

"It's when you lose your 'sparkle'. When you're so fried that the things you used to love no longer make that amazing excited feeling in your gut anymore. All you want is to shut yourself off from the world and recharge."

"Complete exhaustion without caring about things that I know I care about. Wanting to be away from everything and everyone."

"Needing to sit near a wall socket to plug in and recharge just to move!!!"

"A mental fog and sense of disorientation. And a sense of carelessness. A sense of detachment."

When I asked them what they thought of the difference between burnout and depression, they answered:

"In my experience, I think depression *can* come from burnout but it's not a definite at all, and I don't think it's in a continuous sequence of clarity/happiness to burnout/depression. In my opinion, the depression associated with burnout manifests itself in self-doubt... When burnt out, you start questioning yourself and your abilities and/or passion for your chosen path. *Is this what I really want to do? If so, then why do I feel like this? If I truly loved what I did, I wouldn't feel burnt out. Why can't I get caught up? Maybe I'm not as good at what I do as I think. If I was, I wouldn't be exhausted and have had enough of this.* All this type of stuff... All of which disappears after your burnout starts to dissipate, and you start to find your motivation again. That being said it's very possible to be burnt out but not depressed. There's plenty of times I've been burnt out within my profession but very happy in my personal life and not depressed at all. Unhappy in certain aspects of life? Absolutely. Depressed? No."

"My instinctive response is that burnout is a result of your own choice and habits, but depression can be triggered by things you have no control over."

"For me, burnout is often what leads to depression. Burnout is the bumpy road and depression is the destination. A place I end up at that I don't wanna go to and have trouble leaving."

"I have been depressed (down, cynical, not experiencing joy, apathetic/numb) without the exhaustion that I associate with burnout. Burnout, to me, feels like walking through wet cement, unable to self-motivate. But I can have high mood moments during burnout. [Professionally], I associate depression with gut health and burnout with HPA [hypothalamic-pituitary-adrenal axis]. They can certainly happen together though as it's depressing to be burnt out and long-term depression can cause burnout."

Another major difference that I see is that people who are experiencing burnout are prone to believe that if they just leave this job, or take a vacation, or have a break from it all, the feelings will go away. A person in the throes of depression may not have this same set of beliefs, fearing that no matter what they do, they will always feel this way.

In the qualitative research I did, the majority of people agreed that burnout is related to your profession while depression can result from various causes, life-based or body/brain-based. The issue with this for womxn entrepreneurs is our lives *are* our professions, so the line between these two issues can be harder to draw.

On that note, if you suspect that you may be depressed, please see a mental health professional immediately. Whether your needs are talk therapy or medication, you should use every tool at your disposal that helps you and that you feel comfortable with. I know so many burnt out folk who also struggle with depression and I often send burnout coaching clients to talk therapy concurrently. Sometimes medication is the most appropriate answer, and I want you to know that there will never be any judgment from my side about using it.

Untreated burnout can wreak serious havoc in your physical body. I've been watching people's stories unfold for years now. I know people that have recovered in three months and I know people who have taken three or more years. At no point should this book lead you to believe that you don't need the help of a healthcare professional when you have physical symptoms of burnout. In fact, you'll probably need your regular doctor, a specialist or two, and some alternative healing to get through it well!

Until we start to really see these patterns in our lives, it all sounds so contrite – and feels impossible to manage. *But it's not.* The aim of the following chapters is to prove that to you by letting you know that you didn't get here on your own. You didn't create this with the Law of Attraction. You simply have some faulty wiring that you didn't make. You're following some 'rules' of life that don't fit your life well... Let's get into that.

CHAPTER 3

WHAT HAPPENS TO YOUR BRAIN AND BODY UNDER CONSTANT STRESS?

Your brain is the primary 'stress responder' in your body. In order for you to react to a stressful situation, you must experience it. Within milliseconds, your brain decides whether or not this thing is a threat and reacts accordingly. When small amounts of 'threat' end without harm, the brain creates a response that allows us to react less the next time it comes around. As such, you become more resilient to a similar type of stress. It's this beautiful system that works seamlessly without our intervention, every day.

"Psychologists usually try to help people use insight and understanding to manage their behavior. However, neuroscience research shows that very few psychological problems are the result of defects in understanding... When the alarm bell of the emotional brain keeps signaling that you are in danger, no amount of insight will silence it." (van der Kolk, 2014)

When the stress response in the brain is working overtime, it throws a wrench in the works and the brain isn't able to adapt as well as it could before. This, long term, leads to changes in cognition, decision-making, anxiety, and mood (McEwan, 2017).

Now your innate ability to recognize stress has decreased and your ability to make logical decisions is diminished. Add to that some anxiety and a few mood swings and you're well on your way to burning out.

Here's the kicker. Your initial ability to adapt to stress and respond properly is largely dependent on the environment that you were raised in. So again, I'll repeat: *This. Is. Not. Your. Fault.* If you grew up in a highly stressful or even traumatic environment, the chances that your system works well are slim, but don't fret. The brain has enough plasticity to make the right changes, so no matter what you started with, acknowledge it and then acknowledge your power to change it. You might have an extra hurdle, but don't worry, you can jump.

Truth be told though, changes have happened in the brain if you've been under prolonged stress. Long-term stress shrinks your brain (Ropeik, 2012). When I first read an article about this, it latched in, and I thought about it for months and months. I so badly wanted to understand the brain changes that were happening and what to do about them that I considered doing a Master's degree in Neuroscience. I opted for some free Harvard classes on Edx.

Why would I bother talking to you about what happens in your brain during burnout? I think this is important for a few of reasons. One reason is because people seem to have come to an understanding that psychosomatic illnesses exist, but there still seems to be some resistance to the idea that within those psychosomatic illnesses, there are actual physiological changes. Stress is changing your body, actually shifting the function, size and shape of your cells, and adjusting your genetic expression. Even if it's mostly happening in your brain, it's not 'all in your head'.

The second reason is because it gives you a different goal to focus on when you're trying to add things like exercise, meditation, and diet to your life. For me personally, it's easier to exercise when I am doing it to maintain brain plasticity and healthy gut bacteria than it is when I am doing it to maintain my figure.

33

The third reason I feel this is important is because the brain changes can happen before the time that you recognize any physical or emotional changes, which makes the problems not psychosomatic, but *somatopsychic*. I'll explain what I mean by that in just a moment, but the good news is that looking at it this way can help you to rid yourself of guilt and stop the shame blame cycle. When you know that a combination of outside and inside factors have literally changed your brain, you can forgo the guilt and simply take responsibility going forward for upgrading your brain's ability to deal. Just like Dr. Maya Angelou teaches us: "When you know better, you do better."

Somatopsychic is a term that I thought I coined but then saw it on Instagram a few times. It refers to changes in the brain or body that have an effect on your emotional wellbeing, instead of the more traditional psychosomatic that tells us that emotional stress affects the body. I believe that if it can go one direction, it can go the other. This is especially true for patterns and neural networks that affect the development of your brain from a young age. As a child, you had no control over the environment you grew up in and the subsequent development of the patterns and neural networks that resulted. Those patterns and networks are responsible for your ability to handle stress as an adult.

Neural networks, known as 'programs' in some circles, are called 'filters' in my practice. The best imagery I saw to describe filters while reading through the research dealt with brain grooves. You know those wiggly lines that are all over your brain? They change over time. Yep, their shape isn't predetermined. They adjust based on your thoughts, learning, and life experience.

These grooves, or filters, are made up of beliefs that you were taught – usually at a young age. The first time you heard an idea, if you had an emotional reaction, your brain created a mini groove. Then, you heard it again and the groove got a little longer.

Someone else repeated the idea and the groove got a little deeper. As time passes, it becomes a filter. This filter is a belief through which you view the world. It is not based in any sort of absolute truth, although you believe it with blind faith until you stop to examine it.

Since you now have this filter, you interpret all situations through it; anything that you hear, see, or smell that comes even *close* to matching this filter makes the groove slightly deeper. Basically, you walk around proving your filters and beliefs right with the way you interpret life, which is colored by those same filters and beliefs.

Here's what a filter might look like in action.

You just learned how to tie your shoes. It was a way that your teacher taught you that finally stuck. You'd been trying to learn from your father, but you just couldn't figure out his method. You are beaming with pride at finally being able to do this task and thrilled at finding a different route to success.

You go home and say to your dad, "Hey Dad!! Look at this, I can tie my shoes!!" and proceed to show off your new skill.

He watches and then replies, "Ha! That's silly. You're doing it wrong!"

You're crushed, your eyes well up with tears and you run to your room. Later that day, you're sitting at the table and trying desperately to use a knife to cut through your chicken. The knife is big and your hand is small and it's a little awkward, but you're trying. Your older brother nudges your father and says, "Look at little Sally, she can't even cut her own chicken right!" and they have a laugh at your expense.

Then, the next day at school, your teacher tells you your 'a's are backwards on your worksheet.

This is enough to start a filter: "Everything I do is wrong. I don't know how to do anything right."

Now, this is a super simple filter to prove correct throughout childhood. You're constantly learning and you're meant to make mistakes. That's normal, but you've got your filter on now. Every single time you don't do something perfectly, you start chastising yourself. And the groove deepens. Every time someone else criticizes you, even with good intent, you feel it intensely. And the groove deepens.

Just think for a second about how easy it is to burn out when everything you do is wrong, when you believe that you're not good enough, smart enough, or pretty enough. How much easier do you think it is to burn out when your filters are largely negative? I'll tell you: much, much easier.

Your work here will rely upon techniques that aid restructuring of your brain and positive thinking. I am not the biggest fan of 'positive thinking' as it is shown in popular culture. I believe it is often short-sighted and offered at a superficial level. People that start down a road of positive thinking who already have positive filters will have better results than people who started with a majority of negative filters. The playing ground isn't even, folks. This often leads to those with negative filters getting down on themselves for 'not positive thinking hard enough'. I'll repeat myself: This. Is. Not. Your. Fault. If you are encoded with all sorts of negative beliefs, a few positive affirmations aren't going to get you where you need to go. Having said that, you can level the playing field out for yourself, at least on a brain level. To do that, you'll need to find the tools that work best for you and focus on rebuilding your brain circuitry until it's more beneficial to you. Don't worry, I'll give you the tools later in this book.

Here's What Happens in Your Body with Stress

"Cells, tissues, and organs do not question information sent by the nervous system. Rather, they respond with equal fervor to accurate life-affirming perceptions and to self-destructive misperceptions. Consequently, the nature of our perceptions greatly influences the fate of our lives."

— Bruce H. Lipton

Stress, in and of itself, in small doses is well regulated in the body and the brain, and even necessary and beneficial. Say you come into contact with a cold-causing bacteria or virus. The slight boost to your immune system that the pathogen causes to help you fight off a cold is 'good stress'. Say that bacteria or virus decides to multiply and attack every day for three months. The initial boost to your immune system has now become a chronic slightly elevated immune system, which makes you feel lethargic and constantly unwell. Small, regular stresses that give you boosts – good. Stresses that continue long term and wear you out – bad.

Chronic, or toxic, stress leads to lasting changes in the brain. In turn, those changes lead to physiological disruptions in the body (and vice versa). When cognition, decision-making, and mood are impaired, the body's response is to react via the immune, metabolic, neuroendocrine, and autonomic systems (McEwan, 2017). This basically means that long-term chronic stress is affecting *every single function in your body*.

Let me break that down for you. Chronic, or toxic, stress of the kind that I relate to burning out will give your immune system a small initial boost, but eventually weakens your immune system because as this or any other stress continues, so does the response. It's like turning on a light bulb 1500 times in a row and then being surprised that the light bulb burns out. The initial threat that the immune system responds to is easy to handle. That threat repeated time after time after time diminishes the immune system's ability to respond. Eventually, the response goes wonky. This is how researchers relate chronic stress to autoimmune dysfunctions. Your immune system went bonkers after too much overload for too long. Somewhere along the line, a mistake was made and your body is stuck on repeat.

Now, you might be wondering how we might differentiate between good stress and toxic stress. It would be a good thing to wonder about. There isn't a clear view of what is good stress and what is toxic stress because of the filters I mentioned earlier. By having different brain development and different filters, each individual will respond to stress differently, even making good stress toxic for some people. This ties into what I believe is the strongest indicator of health – resilience (or it's updated version: bouncebackability!). Your ability to take a difficult situation and use it as a growth experience is reliant on the filters that make up those grooves in your brain – the ones that you downloaded as a child.

When you are able to bounce back, to see a situation through a different perspective, and adjust your reaction, stress won't bother you as much as it bothers Negative Nancy down the street. It is an indication of good coping mechanisms. This was an important lesson for me. As a resilient person, I often didn't understand why people responded so dramatically to events that I deemed 'normal' or 'no big deal'. It wasn't until I learned about filters that it all started to make sense to me, and I was able to give other people grace and the space to have their own reactions and emotions.

I had a patient who had a fairly stressful life, and with her permission, I'll share this story. She grew up in Poland with a single mother which is highly atypical in a country that is predominantly Catholic. Her mother had poor coping skills, which she passed on to her daughter. She had been my patient for five or six weeks when she came into clinic, eyes puffy, cheeks covered in tears, and exclaimed as soon as we got into a private room, "My mother needs an *operation*!!" and continued to sob.

By her state and reaction, my initial thought was that her mother had some sort of sudden issue that had come up unexpectedly – maybe an accident or a heart attack or something major – and been rushed to the hospital to be operated on to save her life. I asked my patient what happened. She told me that her mother was having a routine hysterectomy following months of bleeding and spotting even though she was well into menopause. There was no cancer. The operation wouldn't happen for another month. It was basically a low risk procedure.

This is where things get sticky. My patient's reaction was real and her emotions should be validated. She also needs, for her own benefit, to be able to handle things like this in life because they will happen. In the state she was in, she was bound to get a cold or flu and be laid up for a couple of weeks. If she responded like this to other life changes, she'd end up even sicker.

I see this in my office every day.

I asked her if she'd be willing to play a game with me, and she agreed. I suggested she use the Filter Method, as I describe in full later in the book, the basic premise of which is to tell the same story a few times through different, consciously chosen filters. I changed the filter for her for the first round. I suggested that she try this new filter: "Everything is okay. Doctors are on top of it" instead of her initial filter "Life is a disaster. My mother is going to be killed in the hospital." She calmed down quickly as she told the new version of the story. I asked her to tell the story again through the filter "My mother's been suffering. The operation will save her from suffering." She calmed down even further. We proceeded with our normal chat followed by an acupuncture treatment where I addressed her emotional state. (Acupuncture has been shown to help the brain regrow and regulate emotions.) She left feeling much better and with a new tool for dealing with life. At this point, I've seen her as a patient for nearly a year and she now regularly uses the Filter Method to check in with herself about the severity of her reactions.

The effects of chronic stress on the physical body can be so varied. Fact vs. opinion on this is also hard to shuffle through. However, here are some of the issues I've seen in my practice that have responded well to stress management: fertility (especially PCOS, amenorrhea, undiagnosed infertility, high FSH and low AMH levels, irregular menstruation), migraines, headaches, recurrent pain, fibromyalgia, chronic fatigue, chronic low back pain, dry irritated eyes, insomnia, thyroid conditions, arthritic conditions, chronic neck and shoulder tightness, chronic sinus infections, IBS, colitis, TMJ, and more.

By the end of this chapter, I hope you are more able to give yourself some grace and realize that your reactions may be different than other people's because of your particular set of filters that *no one else in the world has*. Only you know how you are affected by life's twists and turns. In addition, I hope that you learn to give other people the proper space to react to things the way that they need to without judgment. It's not them reacting, it's their filters.

Highly Sensitive People and Their Propensity Toward Chronic Stress and Burnout

An aside about those of you who are highly sensitive... Because I love to talk about topics that are not often discussed, I thought it was a good time to introduce you to the concept of HSP. HSP stands for highly sensitive person and is an *actual thing*. It's not a label that someone can give another person when *they* assume that person is too sensitive. It's a state of brain function that means you are more reactive than the average person to stimuli in your environment. Your nervous system is working on overdrive. And again, it's not your fault. It's a genetic predisposition.

HSPs make up about 15-20% of the animal kingdom, and this is true across all animal species, according to HSP researcher and expert Elaine Aron, author of the book *The Highly Sensitive Person*. In order to describe the reactions that make up an HSP, the research relies on the acronym DOES:

"D is for depth of processing. Our fundamental characteristic is that we observe and reflect before we act. We process everything more, whether we are conscious of it or not.

O is for being easily overstimulated, because if you are going to pay more attention to everything, you are bound to tire sooner.

E is for giving emphasis to our emotional reactions and having strong empathy, which among other things helps us notice and learn.

S is for being sensitive to all the subtleties around us." (Aron, 2012).

As an HSP myself, I can attest to the fact that being hyper-stimulated all the time leads to exhaustion. I have a difficult time being in crowded areas that are loud. It makes me want to sit down and cover my head with my hands. When I was younger, going to clubs or parties held the requirement of drinking plenty of alcohol so that I could dull my reactions in order to enjoy myself. I didn't realize that I was doing this until well after my party days were over. HSPs, as children, often have a hard time with tags in clothes or seams in socks. I, for instance, will hunt down a pair of scissors if a tag is touching my sides even to this day. I cannot handle it. The sensation of the tag takes over everything and makes it impossible for me to concentrate. I've been known to go into stores and ask for scissors and then stand there and cut tags out of my shirts.

If you are HSP but unaware of it, my theory is that you will burn out faster than other people because you are trying desperately to be able to do all the things that other people can do without taking into consideration that you might need more recovery time than the average bear. I also believe that the chances of womxn entrepreneurs in service-based businesses being HSPs are fairly high. The positive side of HSP is that you are sensitive to the world around you and can often create solutions for people that they wouldn't have thought of themselves. Your set of skills works well in the healing and teaching fields because you feel people's energy more easily than other people do. You can fulfill needs because you can *feel* them. It's part-burden, part-magic.

If you are an HSP, there is a good chance that you've created a couple of filters that need some shifting. In the current working culture in the US, the qualities of an HSP are far from being appreciated. This means that you've probably heard multiple times some form of "you're too sensitive," or "you're too emotional," etc., etc. It was probably repeated to you often as a child as well. Those filters will need breaking down, but don't worry, you can do it.

If you are an HSP female-identifying entrepreneur, you will absolutely need to work on clear boundaries and extra recovery time. When you travel, you'll need a day when you get back to settle. You should limit the amount of one-on-one work that you do on a daily basis to be sure that your sensitivity can handle it. There is no absolute rule for how this should look. You will need to trial-and-error it until you find a system that works for you. One of the first things that happens during burnout coaching with me is something that I call 'life pruning'. You get permission to cut away the pieces of your life and business that aren't serving you and that are costing you *way* too much. This is almost always met with an amazing amount of relief on the side of the client and gives them the space they need to begin to heal.

Suspect that you might be an HSP? Elaine Aron has a great quiz on her website that you can take to find you. You can find it here: http://hsperson.com/test/

Also, I highly recommend reading Elaine's book *The Highly Sensitive Person* to give yourself some perspective and create space for grace. There is nothing more satisfying than reading about yourself in a book that really gets you and makes the world make more sense. Elaine's book did this for me. It might do it for you too.

CHAPTER 4

WHAT IS BOUNCEBACKABILITY?

'Bouncebackability' is a term I coined during a podcast episode a few years back. When talking about stress management, the solution is often touted to be resilience – but that word doesn't feel as fun to me. Let's look at resilience's definition from Merriam Webster:

1. the capability of a strained body to recover its size and shape after deformation caused especially by compressive stress

2. an ability to recover from or adjust easily to misfortune or change

Looking at that second definition 'recover from or adjust', what I think is missing here is the 'sit in the muck' part of misfortune and change.

Bouncebackability (as I define it, since I made it up) is a skill that can be developed, the goal of which is to allow a person to respond to stress in a way that is of benefit to them. It is a combination of resilience, trust, grit, and surrender. Bouncebackability can be applied *way* after a stressful event or a change. It doesn't need to be immediate, and often, I suggest that it not be. Resilience is an object's ability to return to 'normal' as soon as possible and as easily as possible after 'impact'. Bouncebackability includes your ability to first allow space for a reaction to whatever just happened followed up by your ability to *use* that thing as a springboard to bring you back to a state that is *better than before*. There is no set timeline. Allowing space for your reaction, for your emotions, is something that I call 'sitting in the muck'. Sitting in the muck means not searching for a silver lining the moment you have a car accident. It means not creating a positive spin on a situation before you're ready. It means feeling the anger, joy, sadness, or rejection without trying to shoo it away or make it unimportant. You can sit in the muck for a day, a year, a decade – as long as you decide, at some point, to bounce back. I love the word bounce. I love its buoyancy. I love Tigger from Winnie the Pooh. Bouncebackability isn't hard or tough like resilience feels to me. It's soft. It allows time and space for the whole experience. The only thing it asks of you is that you use your life as a series of lessons that better you.

The other thing that I think is wrong with the definition of resilience is this word: easily. Saying that we should always be able to 'easily' adjust after misfortune or change does not allow the space that we sometimes need to break down before we build back up. It also does nothing to build our belief that sometimes things are hard, that it's okay for things to be hard and we can still deal with them.

Bouncebackability is inherently okay with things being difficult, trusting yourself to be able to handle it, and offering hard problems over to the universe when that's the best possible solution. It's knowing when to quit and when to grit. I'm not saying that bouncing back will be easy – just that you can do it. I trust you enough to say that. I've seen you do it. I've read your stories. No matter what life throws at you, eventually, sometimes with ease and sometimes with great difficulty, you can bounce back. The level of difficulty you're facing in any given situation has nothing to do with your ability to bounce back from it. Having bouncebackability means that you trust yourself no matter what.

45

If you find yourself at the bottom of a particularly difficult time in your life, the timeline for your bounce back may be longer. You might need to stay at the bottom of the well gaining strength for your bounce back for a significant period of time. But that doesn't change the fact that eventually, you'll do it.

I need to be very clear about something right here and right now. I have been guilty of saying "everything happens for a reason" more than once in my life, but I'd like to retract that statement from my previous conversations and add this instead: I believe that we have a choice to make after difficult situations in our lives. We can either look at the situation in hindsight and find meaning in it – or not. Part of bouncebackability is finding meaning in the things that happened to you, but it's not a prerequisite. I don't believe that you asked for or deserved some of the shit that happened to you. I do believe that choosing to add meaning to it makes it easier and lighter for you, and thus improves your life, but that's a choice that I'll leave up to you.

Here's what bouncebackability *doesn't* mean. It doesn't mean that you always feel great. It doesn't mean that difficult situations in your life will be met with glee. It doesn't mean that you'll never have hardships.

It *does* mean that you know, no matter how tough life is at any given moment, you will allow yourself space to process and react, and then you will bounce back.

So, by updating the definition of resilience – eliminating the word 'easily', creating space for 'sitting in the muck', adding self-trust, belief in our own grit, and the ability to surrender – we have created the idea of bouncebackability. I often ask my patients and clients to rate their own bouncebackability on a scale of 1-10 in relation to a particular situation. If you'd rate your bouncebackability from burnout today at a 1/10, by the time you get through this book, my hope is that you'll give yourself a 10.

46

Remember, that doesn't mean that you'll be on the other side of burnout, just that you trust yourself enough to believe that you'll get there, no matter how many reroutes it takes.

Measuring Bouncebackability

There's a scientific measure of bouncebackability. I mean, they call it stress resilience, but we already know it's called bouncebackability. This measure is called HRV (heart rate variability). We tend to think that our hearts beat at a regular rhythm, but the truth is that it varies based on our emotional state, our sleep quality, our exercise. It changes when we inhale, it changes when we exhale. The difference between these changes is measured by using a sensor that you can attach to your chest, finger, or earlobe. If the variation between heartbeats is low, it is a sign that your system is in high alert, it is stressed and busy taking care of said stress. If the variation is high, it is a sign that your rest and relax nervous system is activated and your bouncebackability is higher.

If you're a tech type person, this is your jam. I love this stuff. I always love when spirituality and science find spaces where both of them are as true as the other. And, if you're someone who needs charts and measures and proof, HRV is your ticket to making all of this burnout and bouncebackability stuff make sense. The science says basically this (and I'm paraphrasing in a major way; there are thousands of studies and hundreds of books on this, so I've included a list in the back of this book that you can check out): when your HRV is high, after a session of deep breathing and focusing on positive emotions, your ability to handle life in all areas – mental, physical, emotional, and spiritual – increases. Athletes use this to confirm when they should have slow days with training (HRV low) and when they have the energy to push things a bit more (HRV high). You can use it to know when it's time to stay in the muck (HRV low) and when it's time to bounce back (HRV high).

The Heart Math Institute is where most of this information has been gathered. They have a great website with a ton of free info on it, and they also offer measuring tools and apps to help you practice and improve your HRV using meditative and breathing techniques. My favorite thing about HRV is this: it is only measured compared to you. There's no 'good' measurement. There's where you started, where you go when things are shit, and where you go when things are good. The more often you measure, the more sensitive and on point the measurements are. This isn't a contest with anyone. This is about you with yourself.

There's plenty of wearable tech that offers HRV measurements. I like The Heart Math's tool that plugs into your phone because it doesn't need a battery and you only measure when you want to. In addition, it comes with an app that teaches you how to improve your HRV, which improves your bouncebackability. If you want to have full-time measurement and see how everything you do affects your HRV, I suggest you get the Oura Ring. It's an investment, but it will show you clearly where you could spend more time to help boost your bouncebackability. Doing it this way ensures that you'll focus on improving your relationship with your own energy and therefore you'll make the biggest impact with the least amount of effort – the perfect burnout solution.

Not into tech? You can measure bouncebackability without it. All it requires are a couple of sheets of paper, a pen, and your willingness to be honest. This exercise was something that Ewa and I would practice with our clients at our fertility coaching sessions. It's called the Worst-Case Scenario exercise and its purpose is to teach you just how far down your resources can take you. By taking the time to sit and actually plan out your worst-case scenario, you bring a name to the fears that are holding you back, recognize your power, and can give yourself a bouncebackability factor of 1-10 (I hope the exercise itself helps you all get 10s!).

Here's the Worst-Case Scenario exercise. It sounds awful, but once you do it a few times, you realize that it helps you to face truths that you'd normally ignore in a safe way. This particular exercise is used to help you measure your bouncebackability about a particular problem in your life, but the more you do it, the more you realize that your bouncebackability in one area is usually the same as your bouncebackability everywhere. As the saying goes, the way you do one thing is the way you do everything.

1. Choose a problem you'd like to gauge yourself against and take two sheets of paper.

2. At the top of one write: What will I do if I don't do/get what I want? or What will I do if (x) happens? The example I'll use throughout is: make a successful online course. So, my paper would say at the top: What will I do if I fail at making a successful online course?

3. Think of the very first moment that you realize that you aren't going for it and it's not going to happen. Write down how you'll feel. Will you be mad? Sad? Disappointed? Relieved? Be *honest*.

You might have resistance to this if you've been taught to 'manifest by thinking positively'. I truly believe that there is a major misunderstanding in the Law of Attraction and the idea that you can ignore your 'difficult' emotions about something by only focusing on the good is one of the most destructive messages we've received over the years. It does nothing to teach us that we are resilient creatures and can handle it if things don't go our way. In the introduction of this book, I shared with you how dejected I felt when I couldn't influence an entire country's way of being by behaving positive enough. I couldn't 'fix' the energy around me no matter how much work I did. Yes, we create our worlds, but hey... so do the other 8 billion people out there. That has an effect on you! I believe in being prepared and understanding the benefits of being able to hold space for negative and difficult emotions. I believe this makes us both more human, and more spiritual.

In the example: *If I realized that I was going to fail at creating a successful online course and that I'd launch to crickets, I'd be really down. Likely I'd have tears in my eyes and just feel so defeated. I can picture hunching over my desk, feeling heavy and sad.*

4. Write down what you will do *just after that*. We are talking about moments after realizing it's not happening and feeling sadness, anger, or frustration. In step 3, you created space for these emotions. Now you plan the next step.

Example: *After I realize it, I'll probably call my mother and whine a bit. I need more space for this much sadness and help processing, because I'm now wondering if I'll ever be successful online.*

5. Write down what is happening *one hour later*. How will you feel? What will you do? What action will you take?

Example: *One hour later, I'm likely on the couch, under a blanket with a book and a mug of hot chocolate trying to distract myself, while at the same time trying to create space for my emotions to process.*

One day later?

Example: *The next day, I'm still sad. I'm starting to wonder what went wrong, but I'm not ready to look at it yet. My internal self-talk is still pretty crappy and I'm convincing myself that I'll never be successful at anything, even though I know logically that that already isn't true; it's just what the gremlins are whispering.*

One week later?

Example: *A week later, I see someone else's course launch and get triggered. I assume that she's uber successful and has no problem selling out her course, making loads of money and helping loads of people. I start to get curious and look for clues of what I could do better.*

One month later?

51

Example: *A month later, I'm redoing some of the writing of the course. I'm asking for feedback from other entrepreneurs. I'm realizing that I need help and support, and I'm starting to ask for it. I'm wondering: if I just change this one thing, could that be it?*

One year later?

Example: *One year later, I've either forgotten about it and moved on to something else or I've figured out a way to make it work. If I haven't figured it out by now, I'm certainly asking for professional help and tweaking things until they work.*

6. At the top of the other sheet of paper write: What will happen if I do/get what I want?

7. Think of the very first moment that you realize that you're doing it! You're getting what you want! How do you feel? Excited? Proud? Disappointed? Again, be *honest!*

Example: *OMG. I launched my course and I'm going to have hundreds of students. This is totally happening! I can't believe I figured it out!*

8. What will you do *just after that*? We are talking about minutes after realizing it's actually happening.

Example: *Pop that champagne! Mama's celebratin'! I'd most likely run to my husband and tell him exactly what was happening. He'd celebrate with me and tell me how proud he was.*

9. How about *one hour later*? How will you feel? What will you do?

Example: *An hour later, I am in disbelief. I'm thrilled to be helping so many people. I'm thrilled to have a successful online course. I'm just watching the sign-ups with glee and doing prayers of gratitude for my and their good fortune.*

One day later?

Example: *OMG, now I'm nervous. Is this course good enough? Will I provide enough value for money? I'm stressed and a little overwhelmed. I'm hoping that every last customer is thrilled and happy, but I know that's not reasonable. I start questioning if I'm good enough.*

One week later?

Example: *Things are rolling and I'm feeling more confident. I'm still a bit nervous but I'm proud of what I've created and the feedback is largely positive.*

One month later?

Example: *Wow, I can't believe I really did it. That actually happened. I'm so proud and happy. I'm starting to wonder what's coming next... Do I do this course again? Create a new one? I start looking to the future.*

One year later?

Example: *I look back at that time as a learning experience that I can draw from and continue to create. When I really stop to think about it, it's not much different than if the course had failed. Either way, it turns into a learning experience that has immense value.*

10. Take stock. Is this thing that you're choosing to do really important to you? If it is important and you don't get it, will you be okay? Will you bounce back and try again? Do you now know that you'll be okay and can bounce back if needed? Good, then we're done here. Well, not exactly done. Now, rate your overall okayness and bouncebackability on a scale of 1-10. If it's not a 10, keep at this exercise until it is.

Example: *After taking myself through the whole first half of the exercise, I realized that while initially I'd feel sad and defeated, it wouldn't last forever. I could learn from my mistakes and still create something great, even if it strayed from the initial plan. From a year's perspective, I realize that it's easy to see how to use this as a learning event rather than a catastrophe that will throw me totally off course. My bouncebackability is a 10. I'll totally get through this.*

After taking myself through the second half of this exercise, I realize that while the emotions were largely more positive (but not only) in the second half, the ending is very similar, which makes me feel safer to try something out and solid about the fact that no matter what happens, I'll be okay in the end.

This, my dear reader, is bouncebackability at its finest. The example I used may seem light compared to what you're dealing with or might be *exactly* what you're dealing with. Either way, I want you to use this exercise as a method of getting through your fear and to your resilience. The only way out is through. And this is the way through – by facing it, seeing it, naming it, and recognizing your ability to bounce back, no matter what.

Allowing Space Before Bouncing Back

I am a big fan of allowing yourself time to transform emotions. We'd often like this process to be faster than it is (maybe that's just me), but we need time nonetheless. When I say sitting in the muck, what I mean is you experience something difficult and you aren't looking for a silver lining before you've even felt your true emotions of the situation. In today's positive thinking friendly world, we've done ourselves a disservice by always searching for that silver lining before it's time.

Here's a personal example of that. In the summer of 2019, I ruptured my Achilles, which meant months of recovery and a summer ruined. Two planned vacations cancelled. The inability to walk at all for two months. Casts. Hospitals. Physical therapy. Swollen ankles. And a lot of time on my couch. I'm not a great sitter downer, so this was a *major* challenge for me. When it happened, I allowed myself a good three days to wallow in the changes before I started looking for how I could make it good.

Then, throughout the process, I allowed myself hours and days here and there for additional upsets that happened along the way. I remember when my cast came off and I was meant to start walking, I was in so much pain that I couldn't put any pressure on my foot and I was so crushed. I went to my husband's work and sat outside on a blue bench with him sobbing into my iced coffee. I was supposed to be able to work and here I was still on crutches. It felt like every time I went to the doctor, I didn't feel improvement; I felt a setback. That day, I watched *Jane the Virgin* on Netflix for four hours. I also found time to write and meditate, but I wasn't trying to convince myself that it would all be okay.

My bouncebackability factor is high, so I *always* deep down have the knowledge that everything's going to be okay. And yet, I wasn't trying to find that strength when I was crushed and needed time to feel sadness, irritation, frustration, disappointment and anything else that came up that day. Toward the end of the two months, when I was feeling physically more capable and able to think about getting back to work, I noticed that I was still a bit down. My emotions hadn't picked back up to my normal levels and I set myself up for some counseling. Now, an injury isn't the end of the world. A lot worse things could have happened but here's the thing... *it doesn't matter* how big or small your thing is! Your reaction to your situation is *yours* and you're allowed to have it. My reaction to my situation was this and I needed to take care of myself.

We need time to process. Longer than you think. You can send out the silver lining search party before you're fully on the other side, just please don't do it right away.

Same goes when others around us are in pain. While working in a fertility center in Poland, I'll never forget being witness to many a miscarriage. I am ashamed to say that I was one of those people who looked for the silver lining right away and said things like: "Yay, but we know you can get pregnant, so that's good right?!?" Yeah, in two or three months that might be great news but today? No. No one cared. Everyone just wanted to still be pregnant. Their sadness and pain was too much for me to bear, so I tried to minimize it.

Other people's emotions can be even harder for us to handle than our own and we often focus on cheering people up so much that we don't allow them the grace or the time to transform as they need. We want them to see the silver lining for our benefit, so that we can leave them knowing that they 'feel better'. This is rude. It's rude when we do it to others and rude when we do it to ourselves. The right response is usually no response. "This sucks" is enough and it works. So does: "Is there a specific way I can support you right now?" Sometimes there is a way; often there isn't. Both with your own discomfort and other people's, your job is to invite it in. Give it a seat at the table. Let it know that you aren't here to chase it away, even if you aren't its biggest fan. It showed up, it's here and it'll leave when it's good and ready.

Timelines for Sitting in the Muck

If you're looking for a guarantee of when this will all be over, that would be impossible for me or anyone else to determine for you, because your timeline will be different based on: what happened, who you are, and who you have in your support system. Here's one major way you know that it's time to move out of the muck and hop into the shower to get those last bits of dried swamp off your legs: you get sick of the story (or everyone around you does and you find yourself looking for new people to tell instead of changing your tune). When you are sick of hearing and telling the same story over and over again, it's time to move on. I know that you'd love for me to tell you that it happens sooner than that, but most of the time it doesn't. Bouncebackability doesn't require you to be at your best when you're not ready to be there. It simply asks that when it's time, you'll do the damn thing. Ya get me?

With smaller hurts and pains that might only need an hour or two, the sign to move on from the muck is that you've stopped replaying it in your mind unless reminded by an outside source.

What happens when you're stuck in the muck, you're sick of your story, but you can't seem to make a change? *Go get some help!* Therapy. Acupuncture. Counseling. Coaching. Church. Friends. If you don't ask for help in these moments, you end up leaning on bad habits instead. Instead of friends, you choose ice cream. Instead of counseling, you choose Netflix. Instead of coaching, you choose extra long scrolling sessions on Instagram. When you're avoiding your discomfort, you're outside of bouncebackability's power. You've gone off center. When you are aware of the strength of your bouncebackability, you know that you will do what it takes, talk to who you need to talk to, and get help where you need it so you can face the discomfort and make it through.

Deciding to get help depends on so many factors. The two main ones are time and money. If you can make 10 minutes a day but you can't afford counseling, start journaling. If you have the time for coaching but can't afford it, follow a few people on Instagram or LinkedIn who ask prompting questions that will help you gain clarity. (Feel free to follow me: @cait_donovan or @friedtheburnoutpodcast. I also suggest therapists Whitney Hawkins Goodman, LMFT @sitwithwhit and Britt Frank MSW, LSCSW, SEP @brittfrank.) In addition, every single week on the podcast, I have a conversation with someone who has burnt out and bounced back and now helps other people do the same. Go find the episodes on *FRIED – The Burnout Podcast* that resonate with you most and then follow those people! If you have the money but not the time, find someone that works online or has a membership type program that you can do in your spare time without needing to schedule another hour into your week.

If you have neither the time nor the money, you might consider starting with something as simple as deep breathing for 1 minute a day. Small actions like this build up over time. There's a solution out there for everyone. I am *sure* that there's a way to work within your time and money that will help get you where you need to go! If you're not sure how, crowdsource! Whether it be a few trusted friends you ask or your entire Instagram feed, someone somewhere has an answer for you.

CHAPTER 5

THE SEVEN REASONS YOU'RE BURNING OUT

There are, from what I have seen and continue to see in my work and research, seven major reasons that you burn out. I'll go through them here, but before I do, I'd like you to take a minute and sit with the fact that these reasons partly deal with your subconscious mind, and partly with the environment you're in and were raised in, and they are (one more time for the people in the back): Not. Your. Fault. They are, however, your responsibility to change. After going through all seven reasons, part two of the book will guide you through specific exercises for each reason with an explanation of why they work. No matter which reason you resonate with most, you will be offered a way out.

People don't burn out because they are *bad* or because something is *wrong with them*. Most often, the burnt-out folks around us are the ones doing all the good. I never met a burnt-out woman who was not overgiving and concerned with the wellbeing of everyone around her. So, no self-judgment allowed here. We need to raise awareness so that we can start to make changes. We have no control over what is happening until we can notice it, name it, and work to set things straight. If, while reading one of these reasons for burnout, you start getting down on yourself, I want you to put this book down and do some deep belly breathing for three minutes. Come back to it only once you've forged an internal agreement that you won't play the blame and shame game here. It makes those burnout brain grooves even deeper and does nothing to help.

So, read this with grace, sister. Look at yourself and your life from a distance, with curiosity instead of judgment. I'll give a short intro to each of the reasons here and then expand on them in the following chapters. If you feel that you resonate with one much more than any other, feel free to skip forward to that chapter to continue. Let's dig in.

1.   You are a willing participant in burnout culture

Most of us never take the time to sit down and cross-check if the values that surround us are the same as the values that we want to live by. We follow the rules of success from the outside, from society, instead of asking ourselves what we think success, fulfilment and a good life look like. We've absorbed ideas like 'hard work pays off!' and 'unless you prove yourself, your worth is questionable.' None of this is your fault. It's simply unexamined shit we downloaded from the people around us throughout life. Good news? We can examine it and decide how we want to live our lives.

2.   You are spiritually bypassing your problems

You don't necessarily have to be spiritual to be spiritually bypassing your problems. It's probable you're a personal development junkie (like me) and personal development junkies are primed to spiritually bypass their problems *at all times*. Spiritual bypassing in layman's terms is this: something really crappy happens in your life and before you allow yourself to have a response to it, you're already pulling out silver linings and 'looking on the bright side'. The real and justifiable emotion that you breezed past? It isn't dealt with and that's burning you out.

3.   You are living according to someone else's rules

If reason #1 is the macrocosmic view, then #3 is the microcosm. In addition to all the shit you absorbed from the culture around you, there's a smaller, familial culture that you'll have to contend with too. If your family taught you that the only respectable professions were doctor, lawyer, accountant, and you just wanna life coach your way through life, you might be stuck overworking to prove yourself – and burning out while you do it.

4. You're not being totally honest with yourself

Again, you'll see that the reasons you burn out overlap. When #1 and #3 are true, when you haven't examined your cultural and family values, and tried them on for size and then tossed some of them like that dress that just never sat quite right, you're likely out of alignment and you might not even know what you want or how you want to live. If #2 is true for you, then you've not been honest about your feelings, about how things are affecting you. When that happens, you disregard hurt, anger, and pain that showed up to tell you that something needs to change! All this adds up to not being true to you, even if you didn't realize how you got there.

5. Your working environment encourages it

I'm talking your physical space here, the kind of lights that you use, the height of your desk, the colors on your walls, the supportiveness of your chair. Burnt out folk, we like to 'make do'. We often don't like to spend the time and money necessary to take care of ourselves in ways that we can't easily justify. But... *All* those small adjustments and *all* the ways you're 'dealing' every day all day are wasting energy that you need back.

6. Your boundaries suck

Oh, oh. I grew up about an hour south of Boston. I was raised to be 'tough'. I thought I had a strong handle on boundaries because I knew how to be aggressive. What I didn't realize was that the boundaries draining my energy all the time weren't the ones that I used on other people. I needed them for me. I needed to quit overhelping, overgiving, overwhelming myself for the sake of everyone around me.

7. Trauma is trapped in your physical body and you are being unknowingly triggered

This reason deserves an entire book (or five) and there's a few great ones that I'll suggest as we go along, but know this: trauma, even small mini events that you might not think of as trauma, creates changes in the way you are able to react and respond. Trauma often means that you'll get stuck on automatic pilot, always getting mad about things that logically don't bother you, always feeling tense and tightening your muscles when you need to reply to an email, and so on. Trauma was underlying the majority of my behaviors that led to my burnout, and I think you'll find the same is true for you.

If any (or all) of these made a lightbulb go off, stick around because I have more to say on each of these reasons why you're burning out.

CHAPTER 6

YOU'RE BURNING OUT BECAUSE YOU BUY IN TO BURNOUT CULTURE

There is no avoiding the fact that struggling your way to the top is glorified in the US (and around the world). We love an underdog. We love the story of someone who started with nothing and fought their way to success! We love that they slept in their cars and focused only on getting where they wanted to go! It is inspiring to us, and we try to emulate that energy when we are creating businesses. Hustle culture, we're told, is where it's at.

Especially womxn have taken to wearing burnout as a badge of honor. If we just work hard enough, finally we will gain the respect that we deserve. If we struggle and strive as much as the men, we will earn our places at the top. We are copying stories of success that include struggle and desperation. There is nothing honorable about burnout. In itself, becoming successful comes with its own bag of difficulties. Learning how to balance the difficulties that arise as a natural side effect of growing a business as best as you can only ensures that you'll be able to enjoy and maintain that success when you get where you want to go.

That being said, going against the status quo of your culture is not an easy task and you are often wrapped up in burnout culture without even knowing about it. What do I mean by that? I mean: you've chosen, subconsciously, to play society's game without ever stopping to wonder if the things society tells you will make you happy are the things that work for you in your life. The cultures and subcultures you are born into and raised in have an incredible effect on your life choices. One of my favorite things about life coaching is that it opens the door to questioning and curiosity. It creates a safe space where you can explore your own preconceived notions and make conscious decisions to shift the ones that don't align with who you are, or what you need.

There is an old wives' tale about a Sunday roast that illustrates this point perfectly. One Sunday afternoon, a mother was prepping her roast. To do so, she chopped off both ends of the meat before placing it in the pan. Her daughter was there with her and asked: "Mom, why did you cut off the ends of the meat before putting in the pan?" Her mother replied: "I'm not sure. That's how your grandmother did it." So, the daughter, still curious, called her grandmother and asked: "Grandma, why do you cut off the ends of the meat before you put it in the pan?" And her grandmother replied: "Well honey, that's what my mother did." Refusing to let her curiosity go, the daughter called her great-grandmother and asked: "Great-grandma, why did you cut the ends of the Sunday roast before putting it in the pan" and the great-grandmother replied: "Because I didn't have a bigger pan and it wouldn't have fit."

How many of these types of things are we holding onto and repeating because we never embraced the curiosity of the daughter? How many 'rules' of society are we still following because it's easier to just continue than it is to question?

There are a lot of books and methods out there that focus so much on the individual person and how much power they have. They teach you to change your inner world, that everything you experience in life you create. I agree with them, and I disagree with them as well. I disagree because often they ignore and eliminate the fact that your environment has an incredibly strong effect on you. Within each life, each home, each workplace, there are multiple people, personalities and energies that come into play. Our environment is made up of other people and their energy. Until we are able to see this and examine it, there is only so much we have the ability to shift by working on ourselves.

I believe that it is impossible to separate yourself from the energy of other people or the energy of your environment. So, if you have negative people in your environment, you'll absorb some of that and things in your life might reflect that energy, even though it didn't originate with you. We've placed so much emphasis on the individual that we've forgotten about all the surrounding energy.

From birth to age six-ish, you are downloading belief systems and ways of being from your immediate environment. Your brain is stuck in theta wave mode, which basically means that you are in a hypnotic trance. You're taking in the world around you with no method for controlling any of it. That means that all the emotions, thoughts, outbursts, fears, nice words, bad words, and everything in between become a part of your internal fabric without your awareness or permission. This absorbed energy creates deep core beliefs that taint the way you view the world and last throughout your lifetime, unless you take the time to notice them and pick them apart to find out if they are 'true'. (Hint: Nothing is an absolute truth.)

This part of our development sounds pretty creepy, but it's important so that we understand how to function in the society around us. For many millennia, our survival depended on our ability to 'fit in'. So, this brain state was a vital piece of our ability to survive.

If you haven't taken the time to look at your internal fabric, it doesn't reflect on you poorly. Almost no one does, because these beliefs and societal expectations are so ingrained that you never stop to consider they even exist never mind if they are useful or helpful to you. So, when I say that you live and participate in burnout culture, in no way are you to take fault for that or feel guilty. It is built into the fabric of your brain. You might not have been aware of this until *right now*. The good news? If you embrace the energy of that curious daughter, you'll be able to notice and shift all the patterns that don't serve you well.

I'll give you an example. My mother comes from a large family. She has four sisters and two brothers. One of her sisters passed away with leukemia when my mother was quite young. During this time, my grandparents were obviously stressed and focused on their daughter who spent quite a bit of time at the hospital. My mother, during that time, was often praised for being the 'quiet good girl who never needed anything'.

As an adult, my mother has struggled with chronic pain. Because of my profession and life path, we've talked for *years* about how this pain could have an early life traumatic origin. My mother understood this in theory, but never could make the connection between traumas in her life and her pain. She thought she had dealt with it all and she figured, since it wasn't as bad as what some people went through, it couldn't still be affecting her.

At some point, she decided to do counseling and had a memory of being praised for being the quiet good girl and her life flashed before her. Because of this short time when she was three or four years old, my mother had been trying to be the quiet good girl her whole life. She never questioned it because this path was 'good and right'. At family parties at my father's side, my mother would clean up and do exactly as she was instructed by my father's sisters. In our house, when it was time to go out to eat, she never had an opinion on where because she'd always "find something wherever you guys choose".

The filter she created was: "You will be loved only if you are quiet and good." And it forged *an entire life path* for my mother that had nothing to do with her personality, but became her personality over time. My theory is this isn't in alignment with who my mother truly is inside, and that this, in turn, creates constant discomfort which probably started as emotional discomfort but turned physical when she didn't react to it. It's difficult to get your needs met when you decided as a child that you weren't allowed to have any.

Then, the epigenetics gets passed down further. Her traumas become mine and my sisters', because she created these filters that she passed down to us, unaware. The cycle just continues until someone decides to stop it. No one here did anything 'wrong'. Stop and take that in for a minute. It's no one's fault that my aunt got sick as a small child and who could blame my grandparents for being grateful that one of their kids was so self-sufficient?! This is a trauma, but it's not what you might typically label as such.

If you're someone who has been stuck on the burnout cycle, please be aware that the overarching culture that raised you often created a predisposition for burnout because you were taught to act in ways that are outside of your nature and for the benefit of others instead of for the benefit of yourself. You were simply modeling behavior you saw around you.

Here's the takeaway from this: you cannot separate yourself from your environment and you cannot control what messages you got or what patterns you created as a child. If your culture and your family patterns are not in alignment with what you feel is best for your life, but you live by them anyway because you never stopped to question them, you will burn out.

CHAPTER 7

YOU'RE BURNING OUT BECAUSE YOU'VE ADOPTED 'POSITIVE THINKING' WITHOUT REALLY KNOWING WHAT IT IS

You might be thinking, how is it possible to not understand positive thinking. It's pretty simple, right? Deep breath. Get ready for this: it's not.

Positive thinking, as a movement, started in 1952 with the book The Power of Positive Thinking by Norman Vincent Peale. His goal was to change people's lives by teaching them to live as optimists to improve their quality of life. His book was on the bestseller list for 186 weeks, so it's obvious that people felt they needed a positive twist in their lives and benefitted from his book.

Louise Hay, whose work I love, is another proponent of affirmations and positive thinking. In her book You Can Heal Your Life, Hay took the positive thinking movement and applied it to the body. She related certain problems in the body to emotional processes, such as hip pain meaning you have a fear of moving forward in life and so on. There are hundreds and thousands of testimonials online of people who have been helped by her methods.

Following that, the next big bump for the positive thinking movement was the world's introduction to the Law of Attraction in The Secret by Rhonda Byrne. The Secret's tagline is: 'Feel Good, Change Your Life'. And again, it's easy to find stories online about people who have ended poverty, healed fibromyalgia, and married their dream partners by using the rules of the Law of Attraction that are described in both the book and the movie.

This all sounds well and good. However, let me tell you right away what my biggest problem with this all is and why it could be one of the factors that is burning you out. Sometimes life is awful. People die and you have to grieve. You lose your job and actually do stress out about how you are going to pay your bills. Find out you have cancer? It's normal to go through a whole rainbow of emotions that aren't likely to stop even when you reach remission.

In such contexts and many more, when confronted with the ideas of the positive thinking movement, it may be difficult to live normal human emotions without feeling guilty, like you are failing at something when something goes wrong in your life. So, what ends up happening? You do what's called 'spiritual bypassing'.

Attention: spiritual types, personal development junkies, and high achievers! This one's for you. The term 'spiritual bypassing' was coined in the 1980s by Buddhist teacher and psychotherapist John Welwood. He describes it as: "the tendency to use spiritual ideas and practices to sidestep or avoid facing unresolved emotional issues, psychological wounds, and unfinished developmental tasks". (Wellwood, 2011) And this, my friend, is a surefire way to get yourself a one-way ticket to Burnout City.

The current science suggests that even low levels of chronic stress are shrinking our brains. Every unprocessed emotion or set of emotions adds to the level of stress in our lives. Some of these traumas are encoded at such a depth that we don't even remember them. But our bodies do. Thereafter, every situation that even slightly resembles the trauma (even in convoluted ways) causes us to have a host of emotions that are natural for us, but may not seem 'necessary' or 'normal' to onlookers... Or even to ourselves! For instance, if you were bullied by a kid in elementary school who had a red backpack, your brain and body will flood with cortisol every time you see a red backpack even if it doesn't cause you think about or remember the bullying.

When those emotional reactions don't teach us to dig in and figure something out, they turn into physical symptoms. These symptoms are called psychosomatic disorders and doctors have a hard time treating them, or even recognizing them in the first place.

I do believe that finding a silver lining after the initial emotions have passed is the best thing for your personal and spiritual growth, but I also believe in sitting in the muck for a bit. Allowing yourself the time to feel whatever it is you're feeling, without rushing to dismiss it ASAP with a positive affirmation, will allow you to transform the energy of the emotion that arose. When you take the time to live through an entire emotional cycle, it doesn't become lodged in your body. It gets released. You let it go.

How do you know if you've let it go or if you're holding onto something? How do you know if you've processed the full emotion? In my view, this looks different for each person, but I'll tell you a story from my life to describe what this process might look like and just how long it might actually take.

It started innocently enough...

She walked toward me with a mutual colleague of ours. He introduced us. I mentioned I was thinking of writing a book and she immediately impressed me with her suggestions of where I should look for more info in the classic literature. Learning that she was a speaker at the event we were at, I decided to listen in to the short version of her course during the plenary sessions. I was enchanted.

Originally, I had planned out which speakers I wanted to meet before I arrived at this conference, so I was scrambling to change my schedule. She captivated me with her knowledge, her straightforwardness and what I thought was her confidence.

For the past few years, my field had held a sense of confusion for me. I did not know how, when, or with whom to deepen my knowledge. For six years following graduation, I had not found a teacher that I clicked with. I had the added difficulty of living in a foreign country. And then suddenly here she was. I was so excited that I ran back to my husband and told him all about it.

By the end of the three-day conference, I had a guru. I had already decided to follow her back to China for multiple trips to deepen my knowledge. I was ready to do anything she needed me to do. It was like puppy love.

Fast forward six months: I am in China with my new guru for a training that would last four weeks. The group of people was great and the lessons were going really well. I noticed she was short with people who took a little longer to learn or who asked questions she deemed unworthy, but I didn't put too much stock in this. She was, after all, my guru. I just listened and obeyed.

The material I was learning made me feel like I was steeped in Chinese medicine the same way I had been when I started my graduate degree. It was a magical feeling and I loved the knowledge I was gaining. I could feel myself becoming a stronger practitioner. I could also feel my own sense of importance growing because of my closeness to her.

For the duration of the course, her assistant helped to set up classes and organize things. He had been learning with her for a few years. A few times, the way she talked to him made me shudder. I pitied him for being treated so harshly. But I trusted her and I trusted that she was doing it for a reason. I looked the other way and moved on.

As I became even closer to her, my guru invited me into her inner circle. I was one of the special ones. I reveled in this position and jockeyed to do anything I could to keep it. She suggested I do a PhD in China. I called my husband to tell him we needed to move. I started planning.

Before long, I was offered a full scholarship with a full-time translator at a school in a 'small' Chinese city, under the condition that I started their program within two weeks instead of the following year as I had requested. When I told her I couldn't decide that quickly to uproot our entire lives, she questioned my dedication. So did I.

I returned to China for the second time, six months later. I was greeted with open arms and the generosity you can only feel from someone you've placed above you. Others weren't so lucky.

The way she spoke to some of her students started to get under my skin. I thought we were close enough to have an honest conversation about what I was witnessing, so I mentioned it. She got angry and I backed off. I wanted to preserve my special status but the trip was starting to bring up some serious questions for me. Was she a guru or just a really smart ego?

A month after my trip, I took some time out from my Christmas vacation and taught myself how to create a fill-in-online PDF form for our patients. I put the intake questions she used in a program she was teaching us into that format, then shared it with the private group of students. I thought I was helping.

In my post I said: "I made this form. I thought others could use it as well. It will be easier for our patients to fill in if they don't have to print, scan and send back." She was on a retreat and I was convinced she would return and be thrilled with the effort I had made. What actually happened upon her return sent me into a year and a half spiral of strong emotions and internal discovery. On the private forum, I received an overly polite thank you for all my hard work. And then a furious private message followed informing me I had 'stolen' 15 years of her hard work. She chastised me, telling me I was petty and unprofessional.

She wrote two weeks later to remove me from her inner circle. I had planned the next five to ten years of my life based on what she needed from me. I was a shipwreck. I had not only lost the wind from my sails, but was stuck in the middle of an ocean.

I started, with time, to connect all the dots. I saw the treatment of her students for what is was: ego-based fear. I observed the guttural pain I felt when she dumped me. Without her, I felt worthless. I questioned my desire for a PhD. I realized I didn't really ever want one. I started asking myself questions that I hadn't asked in two years and was surprised by the answers.

How do I want to practice Chinese Medicine?

What kind of relationship do I want with my patients?

What would I teach people if I was given a platform as big as the one she had created?

How do I want to be viewed as a teacher?

How do I want my students to feel when they work with me?

When I wrote about this story originally in an article for Thrive Global, it had been nearly two years since 'the dumping'. I spent them rebuilding myself and my voice. I was scared. I was in a vulnerable position. Being there made me realize why I chose a guru in the first place: if I could just follow someone else's ideas, I didn't have to be responsible for anything. I didn't need my own voice. I didn't need to speak my truth or put myself out there. I could hide in her shadows and do her bidding without making myself vulnerable to outside judgments.

After that, I started blogging. I started learning again – the things I wanted to learn this time. I returned to teaching students myself. I was afraid. But I listened in and moved forward. I realized how much I had to be the filter for my experience and knowledge in order to reach the people it needed to reach. I couldn't and wouldn't use someone else's filter for my thoughts, ideas, needs, and wants.

I have learned again to be vulnerable. I have realized that not everyone will agree with what I say, but that I can choose to be kind and generous anyway. I gained enough knowledge that I now don't want or need to chase guru status. My true desire lies in helping you be your own guru. My true value comes from having learned this lesson myself.

This process, until the moment I could tell this story and truly feel no animosity, leftover pain, shame, or anything else, took two full years. Two years! I found multiple silver linings along the way to keep myself going, and yet, feeling this all the way through took much longer in my body than it did in my mind.

After about six months, I started saying that I understood; that it was okay. But when I saw her name on my feed, it would bring up those emotions again. A year in, those emotions were dampened, but if I'm honest, they were still there. A year and a half in was probably the first time I told the full story without being blamey – as just a story. I could have told it like that earlier, but it would have meant that I was dissociating from my pain. Had I ignored it completely, it would have created pain in other areas of my life. Most likely in my marriage. It's always the easiest to take things out on the people who are safest for you. And that would have been, well, shitty.

There is so much current focus on 'living your best life' and 'being happy', but it is important to remember that sometimes things are shitty and that's part of life too. The pressure to maintain a positive attitude at all costs is a source of burnout for too many of us. It's causing us to avoid our problems, pretend that we're over them before we really are, and those emotions are sitting in our bodies and brains and burning us out.

There's a balance between spirituality and practicality that I must show you here. As a long time student of spiritual principles and a chick from a run-down city, I have an interesting blend of strong spiritual beliefs grounded in an extremely practical nature. I didn't grow up with a silver spoon in my mouth and I can't count the drug addicts I know on two hands (or two hands and two feet for that matter).

It bothers me that spiritual principles are often shown outside of the context of real people's lives. The ability to use spiritual principles properly and with true benefit requires a clear, confident mind that a lot of us just simply weren't gifted with in the brain-forming years of 0-6, nor were we given a chance to develop it thereafter.

This is another motive, in my mind, for writing this book. If you've been intrigued by the Law of Attraction and positive thinking, but you haven't been able to crack the code, there's a reason for that. We need to get your mind right first, to clear the traumas that cloud you, and then you can focus on the rest. As it stands at the moment, spiritual principles have a loud voice on a big stage. The result of that is people coming to my office feeling shame and guilt for not being 'good enough' at the spiritual principles that they might lead to happiness, success, health, and ease. One of my podcast guests, Ashley Rose, a transformational life coach, said it best: "I was stuck on a hamster wheel of self-help, not getting anywhere."

If it was all so effing simple, the world wouldn't be so effed up. But here's the thing, I'm as effed as the rest of you, so we can go through this together. I read things on Instagram all the time that tout: "You aren't broken!" and "You are a magical unicorn!"

And don't get me wrong. This all sounds so lovely. But... But... We are all a little broken, and our inability or lack of willingness to look at those broken bits and go through the pain of putting them back together (or tearing them off completely) is what is holding us back. You must face yourself fully and honestly to get to a place where the spiritual principles actually start working.

CHAPTER 8

YOU'RE BURNING OUT BECAUSE YOU'RE LIVING ACCORDING TO SOMEONE ELSE'S RULES

Growing up, you are given a 'book of rules' by your parents or other adults in your life and you follow it, religiously most often, without question. In my family, there were a lot of rules around noise. No phone calls after 9:00 pm, no toilet flushes after bedtime, no interrupting when the TV is on, etc. There were times that my father leaned out the window and spewed profanities because the neighbors weren't following *his* noise rules.

I grew up thinking that everyone lived like this. My father did his part as well. He held these rules for himself. Every morning, he wakes up around 4:30 am and in order to not wake us, he takes a quick shower, gets dressed and leaves the house to go have breakfast at the local diner with his buddies. He does this out of consideration, so we can sleep. He's even quieter than the proverbial mouse.

This was hard for me in college because I didn't understand how anyone could just walk around making noise while someone else was sleeping. It wasn't until I spent loads of time living with all sorts of different people that I realized not everyone has that rule. Until I really grasped that, I was *always* annoyed at roommates. Didn't they know how to be quiet?!?!?! *So rude!* Or not, depending on what rule book you got.

When you have downloaded rules that don't suit you perfectly, you often end up wondering if this is what life is meant to feel like. You were told that if you followed these rules, you'd be satisfied, fulfilled, happy. You're doing all the right things but it doesn't seem to be hitting home. You're burning out but *everything is good* and you *love your work*.

You were given a template by which to live your life and it turns out that it's not the perfect template for you. The problem? You have no idea that you're living on this template and therefore no knowledge that you can *choose* to change it.

In some cases, you can 'choose' the opposite template of what you had, and it can be confusing because you're doing the opposite of what you were taught, but it's still not working. This is what happens when you don't take the time to examine these templates clearly. You either repeat them or rebel against them, and neither of those options asks you what you really want.

My parents chose time over money. The fact that they were always so available to me is a huge part of my success in life. Even though I saw the value in this, I could not agree to struggling financially, even if it gave me more time. So, the templates I rebelled with were: make more money and do impressive things. I chose acupuncture school in part because it was still a Master's degree, at least.

I created two life mottos for myself based on a rebel template while I was first away from my family during acupuncture school in California. One of them is: "just buy the ticket." I learned young that when I bought the ticket to the grand situation, somehow the money would show up. Someone at the bar would need a weekend off, and I'd get the prime Friday *and* Saturday night shifts and pocket an extra 500-600 bucks in two days.

The second of my life mottos is: "do things that make good stories." And boy, do I have stories. My life, without bragging, is interesting. I've done cool things because doing cool things is a value of mine. At some point, I got this twisted and started doing more and more things on the template: "do things that impress people." That's not the same thing as doing things that make good stories. Some of the best stories I have are of my bloopers, mistakes that happened in everyday life. They aren't all related to big trips, risks, or magic that I've seen medicine do (although I do love all of those).

Doing things that impress other people is a Sisyphean task. That boulder never gets lighter and you never make it to the top of the hill. There's no stopping and enjoying the view, and it's a slippery slope to burnout every time.

For me, the way around being stuck repeating or rebelling is to know yourself, on a deep level. There are many methods for doing this and none of them is perfect for everyone. (News flash: there is nothing that is perfect for everyone, not even 64oz of water a day.) So, it may take some time for you to find the system that works best for you. My favorite way? In-depth personality tests combined with feedback from people I love and trust.

How is this factor different from the one about burnout culture? Burnout culture covers the *big* societal rules. Here, we are talking about your immediate family, the expectations of those people closest to you, and the things they specifically told you do to in order to be happy, successful, healthy, etc. How many family patterns are continuing because you've never stopped to shine a light on them?

CHAPTER 9

YOU'RE BURNING OUT BECAUSE YOU NEVER LEARNED TO BE HONEST WITH YOURSELF

I use the word 'bullshit!' a lot with my clients and patients because it's so obvious to spot the lies you tell yourself from the observer's seat. You aren't lying to be malicious. You lie to help yourself ignore those inner nudges, to ignore your intuition, to avoid reacting to your emotions. You lie to maintain the status quo and avoid disappointing people. You lie to me when we talk not because you plan to, but because you're simply repeating the lies that you tell yourself, that you heard in your environment. Until I bring it up, you've usually convinced yourself that what you're saying is true.

I noticed that I was lying to myself about six weeks after I started writing this book. I sat down for a week in Croatia and wrote the first draft of what would become *The Bouncebackability Factor*. When I got back, I had big plans to continue, but I didn't open the document again until over a month and a half later. When I did, it was because I noticed I'd been lying to myself.

I know this book is important and needs to be written. I know have Dear Abby type wisdom that helps people and can help even more if I can complete this and get it in the right hands. I've been working so hard on building a platform and choosing a niche that I haven't been honest with myself about what I'd *really* love to do. I want this book and the platform it will help to create to change burnout culture, but I'm afraid to say that out loud because it sounds so... *big*. I was lying to myself calling this a side pet project when really it's my heart and soul poured onto paper for the world to see.

I'm writing a book about burnout and setting myself up for *another* burnout. LOL. The irony.

So, at a local restaurant in Prague, while eating beef tartare during dinner with my husband, it dawned on me what a little liar I'd been. As we finished our mains, I called myself on my own BS. I admitted to myself how important this is, how badly I want to get it right, and how strongly I feel the need to write it, publish it, and get it into the hands of as many people as I can. I knew it was true when I was having that internal conversation. It made me feel scared, but as I ordered dessert, I realized I also had this sense of... complete relief.

When calling other people out on their BS, I have come to learn that I can expect one of the following responses:

1. **Relief**. This one is my favorite because it opens the best, most fruitful conversations. I often hear things like, "Ugh, finally someone said it out loud," followed by a host of information that allows us to make a breakthrough. Usually, this is accompanied by feeling validated, seen, and understood. This is majorly important in my work. Your experience is valid. I see you. I might not understand exactly what you are going through, but I can witness and understand the emotions that go along with it. This level of acceptance allows people to open up and see their situation from different perspectives because they don't feel like they need to defend their experience from you.

2. **Annoyance/Anger**. This one is also good because usually it doesn't last long and we can come around to discussing it the next time we chat. It is generally replaced with curiosity, which is my favorite mind space to be in. There is nothing, in my opinion, more powerful than what Zen Buddhists refer to as 'beginner's mind'. Beginner's mind is the idea that we can view a subject, a situation or a feeling with no preconceived notions. This mind space allows people to come up with creative solutions instead of seeing a finite number of options.

3. **Counter-argument**. I like this one too. (Sensing a theme here?) I love a counter-argument because I am not always right. I could be misreading the situation. Then if I meet the counter-argument with a sense of curiosity, it is generally rewarded with a greater understanding on both sides of the table. This is also powerful because it allows me to see what my patient or client is really feeling. This often leads to a huge moment of clarity for a patient. Picture this typical situation. You get asked where you want to eat. You say you don't care. Your friend suggests pizza. You realize you don't really want pizza. You might not know what you want yet, but after you refuse Indian, Chinese and burgers, you have a clearer view. Counter-arguments are great for gaining clarity when you aren't quite sure what it is you want or need to move forward.

4. **Disbelief/Shutdown**. I don't like this one very much. Sometimes people don't want to be seen and will do anything to hide. These folks are best suited to someone else. I feel complicit when I allow you to hide and lie. This is the moment I realize that we aren't meant to work together. I'd rather you fight with me than disappear. This often happens when people really aren't aware of any sort of possibility of a connection between their mind/body/spirit/life. It also happens when people are stuck in a victim mentality and don't want to take responsibility for what

happens next. No one is coming to save you. You need to be able to reach down and give yourself the hand that will hoist you up. If you aren't willing to see or do that, our work together won't last long.

This aura of BS that most of us carry around has an incredibly potent effect on our health, our relationships, our self-confidence, our job or career ... Need I go on? And why is that you might ask?

Think about a moment, in your recent history, when you knew someone was bullshitting you. What kind of bodily response did you have? As a funny aside, while typing this, I had a phone call from T-Mobile, my mobile service provider. The woman on the other end reminded me that my contract had just ended, so now she's worried that I'm overpaying. This just made my stomach turn. Not because I was overpaying but because I never had a contract with them. I've been on a pay-as-you-go plan for four years. So, she was trying to sell me back into a contract that I never had in the first place. It makes me feel icky when people lie like that.

BS turns my stomach and makes me feel gross. I feel like my own integrity dropped just by being on the phone with her. And this, my friends, is what happens when you BS yourself. You lose integrity in your own eyes. You stop trusting yourself. And if you've stopped trusting yourself? No wonder that you're ignoring those emotions and nudges. You don't believe they are correct!

This work you're about to do of restructuring your life to recover from burnout will require a depth of honesty that makes most people uncomfortable. This is one of the reasons I recommend not going through this alone. It is much easier to maintain the lies within your own mind when there isn't someone out there that is available to challenge them.

There is a lot of guilt and shame wrapped up in admitting things you don't want to admit, even to yourself. The idea here isn't to create more guilt and shame, but to find the space to be real and honest with yourselves. When you air it all out, you take away shame's power.

You can accept what you have done until this point, forgive yourself and move on. Blame and shame have no place in your health plan. Be honest. Air out the shame. Create space for true change. Tell the truth about what you want, why you want it and how you want it. Then, follow those values. It'll keep the light burning.

CHAPTER 10

YOU'RE BURNING OUT BECAUSE YOUR PHYSICAL ENVIRONMENT ENCOURAGES IT

For the purposes of this section, when I say 'environment', I'm talking about your immediate surroundings, the place where you spend the majority of your day. The way your physical environment looks, sounds, and feels to you, the level of privacy (or distraction) that it affords you, and the feelings of safety (or lack thereof) that it creates all have a massive effect on how easy it is for you to burn out.

We often don't even know how we feel about our physical environments because we pay so little attention to it. When you sit at the same desk day after day, all the small details fade away. The fact that your chair is uncomfortable or that you hate the paint color on the walls becomes less important to you over time and turns into yet another thing in your life that you 'deal with'. Part of recovering from burnout is eliminating as many things as possible that you're 'handling', 'dealing with', 'fine with' and 'putting up with'.

When you notice the small changes you can make and the massive impact that they have, you'll be empowered and gain some energy back! As an entrepreneur, it's you, your desk and your laptop. Do you need a declutter? Some fresh paint? A few days in a coworking space? A better attitude?

We moved into a new apartment in April 2019 and my desk got put into the corner of the guest bedroom. I am uber practical by nature and the desk fit there, so it stayed there. After working at the desk for a few months, I noticed that I was frequently annoyed by how dark that little corner was. When I was still burnt out, I would have immediately been annoyed and told myself that it fits here and that there's no better option – so if you're saying that to yourself right now, know that I hear you! Being recovered from burnout and knowing how important this is, I started looking for creative solutions.

I realized that if I shifted my desk so that the wall was behind me and the windows to my left, I'd have a lot more light. It would mean that the desk was facing the center of the room and that some wires would be hanging off the back. A few years ago, I would have never agreed to that because I thought it was 'wrong'. When I say wrong, I mean that I was taught wires and other untidiness should be hidden. I had internalized this belief to the point where I didn't realize I could put my desk wherever I damn wanted!

So, I did it. I moved my desk and bought some fancy wire organizers to allay my inner Virgo. As soon as I sat down at my desk in its new position, I felt better. I could see the trees out the window. I could talk to coaching clients with some light on my face without buying a ring light or looking like I'm hiding in the shadows. When I look back at some of my Instagram and Facebook posts from that time, I notice that I was hiding in those too. Feeling good in your space is *so damn important* to feeling good in your business!

There is one more reason that the newfound entrepreneurial environments create so much havoc in our lives. In the book, *Stress and Burnout in the Human Service Professions*, Farber writes: "American workers have become increasingly disconnected and alienated from their communities, and increasingly insistent up attaining personal fulfillment and gratification from their work. T... combination of these two trends has produced workers with higher expectations of fulfillment and fewer resources to cope with frustrations – a perfect recipe for burnout" (Farber, 1983).

Becoming disconnected from our communities has also been noted as one of the many factors that influences someone's propensity for depression. It has been said that lack of connection is as bad for us as smoking or high blood pressure. As an entrepreneur, you're likely doing a lot on your own and that might feel great, especially in the beginning. However, it is easy to feel isolated, even as an introvert. Sometimes, we need some other energy around. If the physical environment where you work doesn't include humans outside of your family, it would do you good to nurture friendships and community in a way that allows you to feel supported.

In order for your environment to feel supportive to you, there has to be an intentionality to creating said environment. As an entrepreneur, this is great because you have so much control over what you put, keep, and change in your space. I know that for some of you reading, it will be easy to skip over this part because you feel like dealing with your templates or stepping away from burnout culture will make a bigger impact. I ask you to look around your office today and make one small change. Notice its effect. This is powerful and aids every other aspect of burnout prevention and recovery.

CHAPTER 11

YOU'RE BURNING OUT BECAUSE YOUR BOUNDARIES SUCK

We can talk about all sorts of assertiveness training and it's a necessary bull to tame: you do need to know how to say no, but that isn't the whole story. Assertiveness training is popular. There are loads of books on this topic. You learn graceful ways to say no. You start building boundaries. You create an arsenal of ready-made responses that work every time. You probably keep them in a list on your phone so you can reference them when necessary. You will feel better and start to have a stronger opinion. It works.

Here's the other part of that story. Once you decide to become assertive, people might not like it. Part of creating proper boundaries is not only setting the boundary but dealing with the fact that the boundary will upset some people, and worse, that some people won't respect it. Being able to do this makes you bouncebackable and less prone to burnout.

I see this over and over again. You've decided to say no. So you do. And then someone is mad or disrespects your boundary. And you're *pissed*. Can't this person see that you are just trying to create your boundary here?!?! I mean, you *have* to protect yourself! It's for your health! Then, out come the memes about ridding your life of toxic people, and how when someone disrespects your boundaries, that's grounds for immediate dismissal! I'll ask you here to give people some grace.

If you've acted the same way for many years, and then you change your tune, change the rules of the game without letting anyone know, and then you spring it on them, it's going to cause discomfort. Causing some discomfort or feeling some discomfort isn't inherently a problem. It is part of life. What I want for you is to be aware that when you shift your boundaries, you will need to reinforce them a few times before people adjust and you might catch some flack as you go. Part of having high bouncebackability is allowing space for grace – both for yourself and others.

Assertiveness training is often accompanied by self-righteousness, because creating assertive boundaries makes the people-pleasers among us very uncomfortable. With creating assertive boundaries comes a belief that you only have to push through that discomfort and the story should end. Here's the harsh truth. No one has to like or respect your new boundary. If you notice people acting poorly, you get to choose to maintain relationships with them or not. There's no good or easy answer to this. It's a shitty part of personal growth that no one addresses clearly.

In my life, I use the Three Strikes Rule for building boundaries. I give people at least three tries to adjust, and after the second strike, I will go through the additional discomfort that it will cause me to have a frank discussion with them about my expectations in the future. If, after two strikes and a frank discussion, they blatantly ignore my requests and boundaries, I let them go. This may mean stopping contact, but most of the time, it simply means engaging less. If after two strikes and a frank discussion they make a mistake and apologize, I'm willing to keep going the distance but we all know the adage: the best apology is changed behavior.

Here's the *real* boundary-building that no one is talking about, your 'inner boundary'. This is not about learning how to say no. It's not about learning to be assertive. It's about learning to let other people handle their own shit and about learning not to abandon yourself. You, in order to have great boundaries, must trust other people to handle their own shit. Your job is to worry about you (unless you're a parent – then, worry about your kids until a certain point). But if you find yourself in the midst of 'I'm a Good Person syndrome' or like my husband likes to call it 'Mother effin' Teresa syndrome', you're paying too much attention to other people's problems and not nearly enough to your own. That means that you are overstepping *your own* boundaries, abandoning yourself and overstepping other people's boundaries at the same time. Not by demanding that they help you or do something for you, but by not trusting them to be capable of handling themselves. You are overstepping by judging them and deciding that what they have going on is not good enough, so you'll help them fix it. You're overstepping because you see that their lives could improve and you're just the one to help improve it. (Maybe I'm projecting here!) You are overstepping because their issues cause *you* discomfort and you want it to stop. You're overstepping when you 'just want to help'.

Here's the thing: if they haven't asked you for help, keep your energy to yourself! When you overstep in this way, you are abandoning yourself (and thus crossing your own internal boundaries *away* from yourself). You're not being invaded, but you are opening the door and hopping the fence into someone else's garden. You're not trusting the people around you. This holds true for mothers and grown children, husbands and wives, and friends.

This was a central focus of the way I lived my life until I was about halfway into writing this book. I learned this about myself when I was today years old. I spend so much time acting in ways that I think people need me to act that I've forgotten who I am and how I would act when I am on my own.

I started this book on a solo writing retreat in Croatia and it took me a few days to find a rhythm. I had to ask myself every morning what I should do first. I didn't exercise first because my husband wanted to. I didn't eat first because my friend wanted to. I didn't have anyone else to pace my day for me. And for a hot minute there, I was lost.

I realized during this time that this is why I love being alone. When I am with other people, I do so much internal adjustment and spend so much time trying to anticipate what your energy might need that I end up completely ignoring my own. Then, I get tired and irritated and quite possibly snap at you, and you just think I'm having a bitchy day. I'm not. I just don't trust you to still love me if I want to do something different from you.

Especially true in the 'be of service' spiritual world, it's hard to know when you are actually being of service and when you are sticking your nose places it doesn't need to go. This bothered me in other people long before I saw it in myself (go figure... LOL). Especially in Polish culture, the tendency is for mothers to overnurture. It's effing exhausting. Every time we are at my in-laws, my father-in-law puts food on my plate even after I've explicitly said I'm finished eating and my mother-in-law gives me tea when I've said I don't want any. They just want me to be comfortable! That's what they say. But they don't listen to me. They aren't comforting me for my comfort. They are comforting me for *their* comfort. So that when I leave, I will tell people how generous and kind they are.

This is such a tricky thing because: is it really a problem to give someone tea if they told you they don't want any? They aren't doing anything *mean*, but yet still, the answer is yes. Sometimes we overgive because we are afraid that other people aren't speaking up about their needs because we don't speak up about our own. Just because you don't trust yourself to speak up when someone asks if you want water doesn't mean everyone is like that. It's not your job to wander the earth overgiving things to people that they don't want or need.

Recently, a friend spent some time in India and became close to a local family that she met there. The son really wanted to go to university abroad, which was an impossible task financially for his family. She can afford to make this happen, so she contacted a local doctor, a friend of the family, to ask the best way of getting him the money to do that. The doctor's response? If you give them the money, the rest of their community will ostracize them, so while you think you are doing a good thing and making yourself feel good by being charitable, you will be ruining their sense of community and belonging. I find that this is often the case when we are overgiving with reckless abandon. We are so focused on the good we can do that we fail to take into account that we might, at the end of the day, not be helping at all.

This is often referred to as White Savior Syndrome and looks like all the ways that white (mostly Christian) ministries have travelled the world and looked to 'save' indigenous people, instead causing disease, upset, and loss of culture in the peoples they claimed to want to serve. Your overstepping may be doing harm, even if that is not your intention. The best way to avoid this is to follow the rules of helping that I was gifted by a great teacher of mine, Lillian Pearl Bridges, during a session she did for me a few years back:

Rules for Helping

1. Help only when asked for specific help. If you see someone floundering, instead of offering a specific thing, try asking, "How can I support you right now?" and allow them the space to figure out what they need and inform you. Don't assume you have the

answer to their problem, and unless someone is in danger, don't offer unsolicited help. This goes for online forums too. How often have you asked a question in a big group online and had 63 answers, 62 of which *didn't even answer the question you asked*? It's natural for all of us to center ourselves and show up with what we know and believe. It's also, most of the time, not helpful.

2. Help when you already have the time in your schedule. If it will cause you to shift your schedule in any way, be sure that it is with *ease* and *desire* that you can do so. Overpacking your schedule with other people's needs is a surefire way to burn out *and* feel resentful (which science says is more toxic for the body than anger!).

3. Help when you have a *true desire to give*. If you're already thinking about what you'll get out of it or what favor you'll be able to ask for in return, *stop*. Helping should come from a place of service, which is why the first two rules are so important. If you have any inclination (usually it comes up as resentment or frustration) that you don't actually want to help, then don't. I know this makes people uncomfortable and I know you don't want to say no, but the alternative is flooding your brain and body with cortisol and resentment and if you're burnt out, you don't have time for that!

Exceptions to the Rules for Helping

These rules often seem harsh to people and I get a lot of 'yeah, buts...' when I teach this. There are *always* 'yeah, buts...' to every set of rules. Here are a few exceptions to the three helping rules I borrowed.

The first exception is: tasks your kids can't do yet. While I honestly believe as a non-parent that almost everyone I know does too much for their children (the internet is about to murder me), there are things that they cannot do for themselves and it is your job as a parent to teach, guide, and assist them.

The next exception is: emergency situations of any kind. If you see a car accident in front of you and someone needs to pull over and dial 911 to save someone's life, pull the damn car over. Your day will wait, things will get rearranged, people will deal, for better or for worse.

And that sums it up. It feels mean to tell you that all your 'helping' might not be that helpful, but the sooner you realize it, the easier it will be for you to release your lead foot from the helping pedal and get back on track to taking care of your own knot. This practice, over time, teaches you exactly where your physical and energetic boundaries lie and make it *much* easier for you to make decisions on how to spend your precious resources and come back from burnout.

CHAPTER 12

YOU'RE BURNING OUT BECAUSE YOU HAVE UNRESOLVED TRAUMA

As I write this book, I am teasing out everything that has happened to me and working through things that I need to in order to heal myself. The more I read, write, and research, the more I keep coming back to the idea of trauma. I am not qualified in a traditional sense to talk about trauma but here's what I've learned, know, and feel.

I've had an overall good life so far. More positive than most. I also didn't have a huge number of instances that would have caused major traumas as we think of them traditionally. No early deaths, no abuse of any kind, no hunger or neglect were a part of my life. Because of the fact that the trauma that affected me wasn't '*big*' trauma, I ignored it. Because other people had it worse, I didn't allow myself to react to my own stuff. I decided that my life was good and it meant that I wiped away all the things that might have been not so great. But yet, as it does, some trauma landed in my bones and needs to be shaken out.

Trauma, to me, is a significant stress response to a situation in life that you never fully process and it gets stuck. It can be 'serious' trauma like car accidents or abuse of any form, or it can be less serious trauma like being shushed repeatedly during TV shows. The degree of trauma isn't important here; what matters is that any stress response that gets stuck in our bodies will cause us to form reactions and behaviors throughout our lives that use up extra energy and can lead to burnout.

Physically, there are brain changes related to trauma (this goes into PTSD), but even without those more significant brain changes, there are physical changes to the body, including but not limited to tensions, pains, aches, impaired function that are trauma lodged in the tissues. Burnout folks? We are often highly functional traumatized individuals. I don't know too many people with burnout who aren't successful.

We play the game right, we follow the rules, but our body keeps breaking down on us because we haven't addressed the underlying issues in our tissues that are keeping us in a state that allows us to be easily triggered – even when, or especially when, we also seem put together on the outside so we won't even admit it.

I started a second book of personal stories to share with you because I think that stories make things easier to digest and it might create some moments of resonance for you that aren't available when you're just reading a manual or guide. I spoke to my mother about it and even asked an online group for some support because I didn't know how to write truthfully about those experiences. There are experiences in my life, stories about me, things that make me feel shame. For instance, for as long as I can remember, I've hidden food – sweets, to be exact. I remember saving up coins so that I could buy a candy bar at the local convenience store and eat it and throw away the wrapper before anyone could see. Even though I know this about myself, and I know I don't feel good when I do it (I *still* do it), I don't want to admit to what's really happening or the shame that accompanies it.

When I write the words "I feel shame," my whole body tenses up and wants to reject the idea that this is even possible. I don't want to face shame. I don't want to believe that it is part of my experience, so I reject it in an attempt to falsify it. In my logical brain, I have no reason to feel shame. I can explain to you the things that happened to me and how I dealt with them. I've been practicing and pretending emotional perfection for so long that I can't allow myself to believe that this is true about me.

But somewhere inside, I know that the emotion is true and real. I simply cannot admit to myself that it is the case. How can someone as smart as I am feel that way about themselves? I know emotions don't always follow a logical pattern (and one of my favorite things to tell patients is: "Emotions aren't logical!") but I have a hard time accepting that I actually feel all these really difficult feelings somewhere inside there.

Emotions aren't always logical because they are often reactions that are coded and melded into our brains through situations that happened years, if not decades, earlier and have no connection to the present day. They are traumas. We are being triggered. And because we don't understand it, we don't accept it. Emotions like shame are often embedded in experiences that we don't even remember so they don't make *sense* to us. And when we can't explain to ourselves why we feel a certain way, we tend to ignore it, shove it aside, pretend it's not there and then it becomes impossible to deal with.

I've met a few people over the years who I felt that I could help but who only ever made enough progress to be satisfied, but not healed. When I look at this from a distance, one thing is clear: trauma, if left in the body, will not allow us to heal properly.

My first experience with trauma healing was at a two-week Practitioner Level Self-Cultivation retreat in Beijing in 2015. Leading up to the retreat, I was asked to do 100 days of an 'old issues' clearing meditation. I did it diligently, even getting out of bed to do it at night if I had forgotten during the day. When I was at the retreat, I learned that this meditation was stage one and there was a stage two coming that we would experience together as a group. The second stage had us standing around a room, facing the wall, with puke bowls in front of us in case we needed them. I thought it was crazy, but I was intrigued. We listened to our instructions and we did the 20-minute meditation required of us. On the first day, about halfway through, the woman next to me threw up. I didn't see it happen as we were not allowed to open our eyes during the meditation. When we finally came to the end, her bowl had a small amount of thick, black, tarry liquid in it. It looked like nothing that could come out of a human body. She had had a stroke earlier that year and immediately following this session, she regained some movement in her arm. We never found out what was in the bottom of that bucket, but I do know that the sparkle came back into her eyes after that day.

There is no question in my mind that trauma is responsible for some of the reasons we burn out, the reason we people-please, are triggered, are emotional, and find ourselves following rules that don't really work for us. We are stuck in patterns, emotionally and physically that we need to break through.

To sum up, you're burning out because:

1. *You are a willing participant in burnout culture*

2. *You're spiritually bypassing your problems*

3. *You are living according to someone else's rules*

4. *You're not being totally honest with yourself*

5. *Your working environment encourages it*

6. *Your boundaries suck*

7. *Trauma is trapped in your physical body and you are being unknowingly triggered*

The combination of these things leads to behavior patterns that make us susceptible to burnout. I've already mentioned that I believe burnout is both internal and external, but for the womxn entrepreneurs among us, there is a large portion of burnout that is internal. We aren't stuck in hospitals with ridiculous expectations and working hours. We aren't controlled by a boss who tells us we can't go home until he does. We created the systems that we work within and healing from burnout requires that we heal from the inside out. The systems that we have set up in our businesses are *symptoms* of the traumas stuck in our bodies, our beliefs, and the environments that raised us. Slowly, with gentleness, we can untangle the threads that hold us here. We can move through and create new systems, new ways of being that are more sustainable, in our bodies and our businesses.

PART TWO:

BOUNCING BACK

CHAPTER 13

THE ENERGY TO CHANGE VS. THE ENERGY TO STAY THE SAME

"But when you're stuck, the major task is deciding if you're going to change at all. The challenge is finding the ability, in the face of an overwhelming amount of resistance, to create a small change in your life and build on it." — Mel Robbins

This chapter is a direct inspiration from one of my favorite life coaches of all times, Mel Robbins. Mel Robbins has an amazing book called *Stop Saying You're Fine: Discover A More Powerful You*, which lit a fire under my ass a couple years ago and my life has never been the same since. I recommend the audio version – her voice and her cadence give another layer of power to her words.

In this book, Robbins talks about the fact that you *think* that the energy that it will cost you to make a change is *more* than the energy you are currently spending. She argues that the energy that you are spending to maintain a status quo is the *same amount* of energy.

Why? How? Because you are constantly justifying your choices and behaviors and you are spending loads of energy ignoring your wants, needs, and desires. Just keeping a lid on them and holding it down is an enormous amount of energy. If you were to decide to lift the lid, you might find out that you were actually closing down on a pressure cooker and all that energy for change is just waiting there, ready to explode!

So, if you find yourself reading this book and seeing yourself in it, stop right now and *make a commitment to yourself* to be brave and make the changes you need to make in order to live a more fulfilling, less stressful life.

It's best if you make this commitment serious, with a signature and all. You can download and print this form from: https://www.caitdonovan.com/freebie-values

I, _____, on this date _

_____, commit to making small but

measurable steps each day in order to make my life burnout-proof,

increase my wellbeing and health, and be a source of good vibes for

my community.

_____

Signature

Taking the time to make this commitment to yourself can change everything. And while I'm thrilled you're reading this book, if this message resonated with you in any way, I highly recommend grabbing yourself some of Mel Robbins' books and reading those too. The concepts that she outlines about energy made me look at it in a whole new light – and I'm an energy worker!

The thing that I want you to take away from this section is this: right now, it is costing you energy to stay where you are. You're used to spending this amount of energy maintaining the status quo, so you might not feel it, but it's going all the time. Shifting doesn't require *more* energy; it requires using the energy that you're using now differently. Making that initial shift is a challenge and that first half a second feels like a big push but that push is mostly mental. One of the things that I do with coaching clients is something called 'plugging energy leaks'. Before making a change, we look at the places where energy is leaking – being misused, mismanaged, and often ignored. And we plug those leaks with rituals, permission slips, mantras, and systems.

Common energy leaks that you might want to look out for are: overstepping other people's boundaries and helping when it's not necessary to do so, doing more for your children then they need you to do (seriously, get them starting a load of laundry, they can handle it), not practicing delegation, believing that you are the only one who can get anything done the right way, negative self-talk, having a hard time receiving, 'relaxing' in ways that aren't restorative, people-pleasing, or all of the above!

We start plugging these leaks by noticing them first. Do you see yourself in any of those things? If you're a solo entrepreneur, have you avoided hiring a VA for too long because it's 'easier' to do it yourself? It's time to practice delegating within your business. Did you grow up in a house where your mother was responsible for all the household chores and you do the same for your kids even though you can't keep up? It's time to practice delegating within the family. Do you have a hard time accepting gifts (money, presents, time, help) without feeling that you have to 'pay' whatever it was back? *Huge* energy leak and one that definitely needs addressing. Accepting with grace is one of the main skills you need as a female entrepreneur if you don't want to burn out (again). Does relaxing for you consist of scrolling and Netflix? I'm all for a good binge, but it's *not* restorative. Doing a 10-minute yoga nidra meditation on YouTube will recharge you more than six hours of *Schitt's Creek* episodes. It costs an enormous amount of nervous system energy to be in front of screens all the time, so moments where you can close your eyes and rest are important.

Once you know which leaks need plugging, it takes some practice before it becomes second nature but you will get there. There are mountains of energy surrounding you just waiting to be reclaimed. If you've been waiting too long to hire a VA, start with someone for a couple hours a month until you learn to fill their time. Practice delegating by practicing small. I cannot tell you how many women over the years have gone through 'mistake' hirings of full-time or even part-time employees that turned out to be a giant mess because they didn't know how to shift responsibility their way. If you're unable to use the employees you hire, they become energy leaks! So, learn to delegate by practicing. Plug that leak.

If, for instance, you're wondering about what makes rest restorative and wondering what you would *do* to rest well, that's part of the problem. I find that burnt out female entrepreneurs have a hard time just stopping. Stopping is restorative. Naps are restorative. Breathing is restorative. Sometimes, we have a hard time feeling like it's 'enough'. "If I'm not being productive, I'm wasting time" is a statement I've heard from so many people like you over the years. One of my favorite ways to restore myself mid working day is to do a one-minute QiGong Face Washing exercise. It requires no water, just your hands and your face. Here's how it goes:

1. Shut off all screens

2. Sit in a chair with your feet flat on the floor, back straight, but not stiff

3. Remove your glasses if you're wearing any

4. Clap your hands together in front of your face and then rub your palms together vigorously until your hands are warm.

5. Allow your warm palms to completely cover your eyes and hold your hands there for 10 seconds, then 'wipe' your hands over your hair and the back of your neck

6. Let your hands meet in prayer position in front of your heart

7. Repeat two more times for a total of three.

This simple exercise will relax you, allow your eyes the rest they so desperately need, and create space for you to refocus – all in under 60 seconds.

None of these things have to be major. It all starts with small tips like this one and a commitment to yourself to use them. Once we reclaim all the energy that is leaking, we can send it in the direction of healing and recovering. Your burnout will recede and you'll be well on your way to creating systems that prevent it in the future.

What Now?

Here's the good news. Neuroplasticity exists. You *can* change your brain. You can also adjust your mindset, no matter what programs and filters you were given during childhood. You can quiet down the reaction of your nervous system throughout your whole body. You can be honest enough with yourself to see your own patterns and break through them. You can change your environment. You can improve your gut microbiome. All of these factors lead you away from burnout and toward a strong bouncebackability factor.

Here in Part Two, I'll give you research-supported ways to do all of the above plus some more of my own woo-woo ways for your own personal experimentation.

As we covered in Part One, here are the reasons you are burning out:

1. *Willing participant in burnout culture*

2. *Spiritually bypassing your problems*

3. *Living according to someone else's rules*

4. *Not being honest with yourself*

5. *Working environment*

6. *Sucky boundaries*

7. *Trauma*

We will, step by step, section by section, give you the tools you need to unwind the habits that keep you burning out. Feel free to skip to the section that is most prevalent for you, if you choose. Before we begin, I'd like to tell you what science says about building resilience to give you a full picture.

"In order to change trajectories of mental and physical health, it is important to focus upon the use of targeted behavioral therapies along with treatments, including pharmaceutical agents, that 'open up windows of plasticity' in the brain and facilitate the efficacy of the behavioral interventions" (McEwan, 2017).

In this same article, the author names nine things that are proven to increase resiliency in the brain, but writing them out doesn't mean you'll do anything. I'll list them here so that you can see when someone tells you sleep is important, they mean it. Every single one of these factors is important, but we'd all be doing them already if we weren't stuck in patterns of behavior and reactions. Here are the nine things that are proven to aid your brain's ability to change, grow, and improve its resilience: physical exercise, changing your filters, dietary changes, improving sleep quality, improving social support, not smoking, medication, acupuncture, and meditation.

As we go through unwinding the reasons you burn out, I'll refer back to this list to tie in the science with what I've seen work in practice – both in the acupuncture office and with coaching clients.

CHAPTER 14

TACKLING BURNOUT REASON #1
BURNOUT CULTURE

Unless you truly understand why you are making changes and how they align with your values, you won't bother doing anything. Motivation isn't enough. It never has been. If you have filters on that say that you aren't worth the time and energy it takes to make changes, no amount of motivation is going to convince you to make the necessary effort. That's why I begin tackling burnout with some major life evaluations before I get into telling you to move your body and eat better. Sound like fun? It should!

I have identified two major exercises for you to increase your bouncebackability factor when you're fighting burnout culture. Both of them require some time to complete, but once they are done, you will have made more progress within a week than you assumed was even possible. I urge you to really take the time and implement them over the course of the next week. You'll clear through so much bullshit and gain so much bouncebackability that you'll cheer for yourself! Using these bouncebackability tools will automatically shift your other reasons for burning out, before we even get to them.

So, we begin by blasting through to the very core of how your brain interprets your world. We start where you'll get the biggest bang for your buck. This first exercise blasts through 'cultural values' and helps you find which values drive *you*. Some of them might be in alignment with your culture, some of them might be totally different from your culture.

An example of a value that is prevalent in US culture that may be burning you out is: individualism. As entrepreneurs, we often do everything ourselves, and because the US is so focused on people making it on their own, we avoid asking for help until it's too late.

Now, I love proving myself in this 'pull myself up by the bootstraps' way, but I realized a couple of years ago that I do best in a collaboration. I tried creating a podcast before I made *FRIED – The Burnout Podcast*, which was mostly just me talking. Now, understand: I won Most Talkative in my 8th grade class. I'm a great talker, but just chatting to a microphone on a podcast made me feel dull, boring, uninspired, and I often forgot to say things that I thought were important. When I switched to the interview format, I felt 1000x better.

Individualism as a cultural value, I believe, is behind burnout in tons of entrepreneurs because we feel that we've failed when we need support – whether it be at home or with our work. Just today, as I wrote this book, there was a part that wasn't flowing. My bestie was sitting and working next to me, so I asked for her view. She offered one sentence – *one sentence* – and I was sent on a two-hour typing spree that cleared up so much trouble that I was having. As people, we have always existed in groups. We need each other. Individualism is an American cultural value that I personally need to set to the wayside in order to avoid burning out.

The second exercise is an updated version of a Gratitude Journal. Again, gratitude journaling is not something I made up – far from it. It's been suggested far and wide for so long now that I'm not even sure who suggested it first. Here's what I know about how gratitude increases your bouncebackability factor and allows you to keep away from burnout culture: when you make an effort to view the things in your life with gratitude and you feel that gratitude in your body (spoiler alert – that's the update), you are less likely to be swayed by the values and materialism that drives burnout. Having a regular gratitude practice keeps your energy in your body and keeps your energy away from the influences that surround you.

Live Your Core Values

The first exercise is the Live Your Core Values exercise. I did not make it up. This exercise is done by nearly every life coach I've ever met because it's so successful in helping you to create a strong view of who you are and what you want, separate from the society that you live in. (Download your free values worksheet with instructions here: https://www.caitdonovan.com/freebie-values).

The exercise is simple. You are given a sheet of paper with words that describe values. On your first reading, your job is to circle or highlight the values that you feel drawn to, without judgment and without hesitation. Simply scan the list and choose the ones that make you feel light and happy.

There's a large list, so you'll probably end up with 25 or 30. With the values that you have chosen, see which ones are similar, and group them up. For instance, if you choose: *boldness*, *courage*, *love*, *recognition*, and *daring*, you can place *boldness*, *courage*, and *daring* in one group. You should be able to create three to five groups. If you have more, review your list and see if there are some words that resonate less that you can get rid of.

The next step is to look closely at those groups and choose one representative word for each of those groups. This leaves you with –three to five representative words. So, if you have a group that consists of *boldness*, *courage*, and *daring*, pick the word that speaks to you the *most* out of those three. If you've just finished Brené Brown's book *Daring Greatly*, you might pick daring. If you have another group that includes *love, family, grace, happiness, joy*, choose the one word out of these five that really jumps out at you. *Grace* is one of my favorite words, but yours might be *family* or *joy*.

Take those three to five representative words and add verbs to them to make sentences that are action-oriented and inspiring to you. So, in this example, I have *daring* and *grace*. Grace is on my values list anyway and the sentence I use is: "create space for grace." To me, this sentence means that I should afford both myself and the people around some space for *grace* — for forgiveness, ease, love, acceptance — in any situation I find myself. The sentence for *daring* might be as simple as: "be daring," which might remind you to take chances regularly, even when you are afraid.

Finally, list your inspiring sentences in order of importance and refer to them frequently when making decisions; this helps to keep you in alignment even when you're burnt out and don't have the brain capacity to think.

The Live Your Core Values exercise creates a system, a process, a set of rules for you to follow that you can always lean on and refer back to. You don't have to remember them by heart. You can carry them around on a piece of paper or in your phone. Knowing what values guide you make taking action, even difficult action, easier.

Knowing which values guide you also majorly boosts your bouncebackability factor because no one's values are: *laziness, criticism*, and *inflexibility*. When you have your values to fall back on and you know exactly what they are, they will guide the bounce-back choices that you make and help you to choose the first step that you should take once you're ready to get out of the muck. As long as you keep making choices that are aligned with your values, you'll bounce back faster and prevent burnout better.

Here's what the exercise looks like in practice:

1. Choose the values that resonate with you most from the list below:

Abundance	Acceptance	Accountability	Achievement	Adventure

Advocacy	Ambition	Appreciation	Attractiveness	Autonomy
Balance	Being the best	Benevolence	Boldness	Brilliance
Calmness	Caring	Challenge	Charity	Cheerfulness
Cleverness	Community	Commitment	Compassion	Cooperation
Collaboration	Creativity	Credibility	Curiosity	Daring
Decisiveness	Dedication	Dependability	Diversity	Empathy
Encouragement	Enthusiasm	Ethics	Excellence	Expressiveness
Fairness	Family	Friendships	Flexibility	Freedom
Fun	Generosity	Grace	Growth	Flexibility
Happiness	Health	Honesty	Humility	Humor
Inclusiveness	Independence	Individuality	Innovation	Inspiration
Intelligence	Intuition	Joy	Kindness	Knowledge
Leadership	Learning	Love	Loyalty	Making a difference
Mindfulness	Motivation	Optimism	Open-mindedness	Originality
Passion	Performance	Personal development	Proactive	Professionalism
Quality	Recognition	Risk-taking	Safety	Security
Service	Spirituality	Stability	Success	Peace

Playfulness	Popularity	Power	Preparedness	Proactivity
Punctuality	Relationships	Reliability	Resilience	Resourcefulness
Responsibility	Responsiveness	Teamwork	Thankfulness	Thoughtfulness
Traditionalism	Trustworthiness	Understanding	Uniqueness	Usefulness
Versatility	Vision	Warmth	Wealth	Wellbeing
Wisdom	Zeal			

2. Group the selected values into no more than five groups.

3. Choose *one* word from each group that resonates most.

4. Add verbs to each word to create actions.

5. Put them in order of importance.

Now that you have a hold of your list, it's important to actually use it for something. I suggest putting your values down and tucking them in your wallet or keeping them on your phone, somewhere you can access them easily at any time.

Set aside time and commit to a self-evaluation that will help you determine which of your core values are present and active in your life. I suggest doing this over the course of one week. As you go through the week, when you come to a task that makes you huff and puff, ask yourself if it is in alignment with any of your core values.

In the more likely scenario, you'll find that this task has nothing to do with any of the values on your list. It is then your responsibility to really reach down deep and figure out if you *must* do this thing or if you are choosing to do it, knowing it is a burden. (Hint: there isn't anything you *must* do.) You don't have to eat or cook for your kids. You don't have to take care of your dying parent alone or wash the dishes daily. You don't have to do laundry or even wear clothes at home! These are things that you choose to do because most of the time the alternative is feeling like an asshole. This is simply what we've been taught, what we've learned through the world around us. I.e. you're a good person if you... <insert caring for others activity here>. We choose to do these activities to avoid judgment, both from others and ourselves.

In the less likely scenario, the task at hand *does* align with your values and this gives you the opportunity to look at this task in a new light, with a new appreciation that will decrease your disdain and annoyance. In my life, I noticed that I was often frustrated that the kitchen was messy in the morning and I 'had' to clean it. On my values list, you'll find: appreciation. I wasn't mad about cleaning the kitchen; I like cleaning the kitchen in the morning to clear my head. I was upset that I wasn't getting praise for it. My solution? I started literally saying, "Good job! That looks nice!" after I finished cleaning. Sounds silly, but it worked for me!

Keep track of the pieces of your life that do not match your values at all and check to see if there are actions or ways of being that can be eliminated or need an attitude adjustment from your side. I needed to attitude-adjust myself about cooking during a health reboot last year. I needed to do a gut-balancing diet, which required that I cooked all of my own meals. At the same time, my husband decided to stop eating meat. Now, meat was one of the only things I could eat, so I was struggling to create meals that both of us could eat.

After the first week, I stopped and thought: He's an adult. I don't need to cook for him. I was so overwhelmed by the amount of kitchen prep and planning that I failed to realize that I ultimately only have responsibility for my own damn food. I talked to my husband and let him know that while I was on this diet, I wouldn't be able to take care of cooking for him and he'd have to do it himself. You know what happened? Nothing. He understood and I was free to focus on my diet without going crazy.

Once you find something that isn't working for you, changing it might require some difficult conversations. Take a moment to acknowledge that. I've done the majority of the cooking in our house for 12 years, and for this period, I was changing the rules. It was possible that my husband wouldn't agree or that there would be some blowback. People don't usually react well to you finally taking care of yourself because it disrupts their routines as well. If you believe Instagram, it's because they don't want you to be happy or because they're narcissists. About 1% of the time, this is true. The other 99% of the time, they just need a minute to adjust to a new scenario. Change is challenging. We can't expect people to be on board just because we decided something. Please be responsible for your decisions and be aware that they might wreak some havoc – that doesn't mean they aren't worth it.

When you ask someone for a change, remember that they can respond three ways: yes, no, or offering a compromise. In a conversation between Brené Brown and Oprah, they agreed that "you cannot live a brave life without disappointing some people." This is an absolute truth and I don't believe in too many absolute truths. That being said, you might not be ready to disappoint people because of some previously encoded filters from your childhood.

If this is true for you, I've found that the best way to prepare for these types of difficult conversations is an exercise that I call The Devil, The Angel, and The Human. When you have a situation that requires a difficult conversation, there's likely a part of you that is somewhat annoyed, hurt, or just plain angry. This is where the devil comes in.

116

Step 1: Take a piece of paper and write down what you would say to the person you need to talk to if there were *no* consequences for your words. That means you're likely to be downright *nasty*. Go for it. Be as mean as possible. You're going to toss this paper, so really let loose. This part of the exercise allows you to acknowledge your true feelings, which is important for Step 3.

Step 2: Take another piece of paper and write down what the angel would say. Overgive. Be too generous. Be as kind as possible. You'll likely ignore your feelings a bit here. That's okay. It's all part of the exercise.

Step 3: Take a third piece of paper and after rereading both the devil and the angel, just be human. Find the middle ground where you can say what is important to you and why without being a jerk and without being a pushover. The human might take a few tries until you feel like you're able to fully express what you mean in a way that will be heard. It's worth practicing this a few times before the conversation.

Step 4: Have the conversation. Having acknowledged your emotions and seen how easy it is to be 'so kind' that you ignore them, you create a statement that is true and real for you while still being kind.

Step 5: Allow the other person their own reaction. It might not be what you like or want. That's okay unless it's abusive. Create space for grace. Take in what they say. Maybe it'll end up even better than you imagined because there are compromises available that weren't visible from your perception alone.

Practicing Gratitude, The Right Way

If you've taken a self-care journey before, you've done a gratitude practice. The usual suspect is: write three things that you are grateful for before you go to bed. What happens is every day you write: my house, my dog, and my job. Super generic and without much feeling. This, my friends, isn't a gratitude practice because at the end of the first week, you're sick of writing the same things so you don't bother writing anything at all. You conclude that a gratitude practice is overrated.

Done that way, it is overrated. In order for a gratitude practice to help you shift your brain, you must have two elements:

1. You must write *highly specific* things that you are grateful for. The more specific the better.

2. You must have the ability to feel, physically, the gratitude spreading through your whole body after writing something down. If you get goosebumps, you know it's working.

You may have heard of the first element, but chances are you haven't heard of the second. When I practice gratitude, I often use my mala beads. Mala beads are a set of 108 beads used for prayers or mantras in the Tibetan and Nepalese traditions. That's right, I aim for 108 things that I can feel grateful for from head to toe. If I don't feel a bodily reaction, I stay on the bead and think of something else to be grateful for that will create a stronger response. To be honest, I often fall asleep as I do this so I don't always get to 108, and I don't recommend starting this way when you're burnt out. Starting at the all-familiar three items is a fantastic idea.

If you've listened to *FRIED- The Burnout Podcast*, you've heard me say that gratitude journals don't always work when you're truly fried and crispy. If you find that those physical feelings of gratitude don't bubble up for you, don't worry. You can come back to this exercise after you've done some unwinding of the other burnout reasons. No matter what the exercise, if it's not resonating with you, let it go and move onto the next.

When you haven't done a gratitude practice like this regularly, it's easy to feel intimidated. This exercise, when I do it consistently, reminds me of what I like and what I enjoy, then makes it easier to have more of that by making simple choices. When you are a highly sensitive person, it's easy to go through life doing (or eating, drinking, decorating, etc.) what other people want because pushing for what you want is uncomfortable. After some time, it's hard to even know what it is you like in the first place so then you let other people make choices and decisions for you because you've lost touch with what brings you joy. I'll never forget when a patient, post-divorce, came in and told me that she had to pick out furniture and decorations for her new apartment and she realized that is was the first time in 25+ years that she'd had to really consider what it was *she* wanted. She had to rediscover what lit her up, because she had made decisions based on other people's needs for so long and lost contact with her own desires.

If you can't think of things that brought you joy today, I'll get you started. Here's a list of 10 things that I feel grateful for right now, at this very moment, while I type from an apartment in Croatia, August 2018 (and if you're reading this in 2020, let me tell you, yes, it takes that long to write, edit, and publish a book):

*1. Black risotto. I am grateful for the black risotto that became my lunch and dinner yesterday. It is a Croatian specialty so I don't often have a chance to eat it. I **ate it with focus** and **appreciation** and **enjoyed** it immensely.*

*2. My legs. I am grateful for my legs for carrying me on a 6 km run today. Just two days ago I only finished 3.5, but today, my **legs flew** underneath me and made me **feel proud and accomplished**.*

119

3. My husband. Today, I am grateful to my husband for engaging with my family and always making an effort to stay connected. I don't request this of him, but he does it anyway and it always **makes me smile**.

4. Google. This week, I was able to use this magical search engine to find a local massage therapist who can help me keep my body in balance as I spend most of my days at the computer. I'm so grateful to have found someone English-speaking within a mile of the apartment I'm working in!

5. The view from this apartment. Every morning, I open the doors to look out over the Adriatic Sea. I can **feel the excitement bubbling up** as I turn the handle and push. It is so **thrilling** to me to be able to be here right now.

6. Coconut water. OMG. How happy am I that I found coconut water, no sugar added at the local store yesterday? Right now, I can only drink water and coconut water, so I'm incredibly grateful to have found a source for my second option. I love water, but sometimes a gal needs to change it up, ya know?

7. A frying pan. Staying in this apartment alone for a week means I have to do some cooking, and since there is only one saucepan and one frying pan for use, I've decided to only make things I can make on the frying pan. It is making my diet super-simple and eliminates so much choice that I **barely even have to think** about what I'll eat. I'm so happy about that pan.

8. My mother. She made me take typing in high school. She said I'd need it. It was the most annoying class in the world, but thanks to that class and to my mother, I can type almost as fast as I think which makes writing a book that much easier!

9. A week without a bra. Ha! This is funny but so true. I'm either in the apartment writing or at the beach. I packed two bras to take *with me but I don't need either of them! What a **relief** to go a week without a bra!*

*10. My sister's new house. It's been a difficult couple of years for my sister and she just bought a new house that makes her **feel happy** and **safe**. I've **welled up** multiple times this week just knowing that she's feeling better. I'm so grateful she found this house and was able to buy it.*

See how specific that is? I have 103,721,937 reasons to be grateful to my husband, but today, these are the most important. Choosing the specific reason behind your gratefulness will allow it to soak into your body a bit deeper and help you change those neural networks super-fast! If you haven't been able to get into the groove yet with a gratitude practice, I urge you to try this body-based system. You'll feel the difference right away.

Gratitude has also been shown to have physiological benefits as well as neurological, mental and emotional benefits. Because of gratitude, tendencies toward materialism will lessen and you'll be able to reach your goals more easily, making things like sticking to exercise and eating a whole foods diet easier to accomplish.

As I mentioned in the beginning of this chapter, there are usually reasons that you aren't making the changes you need to make to avoid burnout and increase bouncebackability. It's not because you're a bad person. It's not because you don't have willpower. It's a set of habits. It's brain grooves and mini traumas. It's a set of cultural values that sit in your body without your permission that you just react to without even noticing.

By focusing on your values for at least a week before working on changing any habits that you know need to shift long-term, you'll make changing those habits easier and more within reach for yourself. If you're really burnt out and you're scraping the bottom of the barrel when it comes to bouncebackability, take a whole month. Just do one of these two things. Even if you don't change anything else, I promise other shifts will follow without you even noticing. We don't always have to go for the most obvious fix because there's often stuff preventing the most obvious fix from being the easiest one. Let's start with easy. That's part of being bouncebackable – knowing that you have the ability to make that first small step.

Often in self-help books, that first step is too big an ask. It overwhelms me as I read it and I give up right there. So, let's not do that here. The values exercise? It will take you 10 to 15 minutes. And then it will be over. Three whole-body feelings of gratitude? That'll take about five minutes before you go to bed every night. And if you end up doing it once a week because that's all you can handle, it'll help you anyway. You can do these simple things for as long as is necessary to beget further transformation.

I ask you here to be gentle with yourself, to leave space for grace. If your resources (time, money, energy, emotional bandwidth) allow only for a 30-second breathing exercise, let that be enough. Letting that be enough will help you realize that you can let yourself be enough, even if all you're doing is being. You are enough. Start small. Allow it to grow. Water your own personal growth one drop at a time. Burnout won't heal overnight no matter what, so pace yourself in a way that feels sustainable to you, one small thing at a time.

CHAPTER 15

TACKLING BURNOUT REASON #2 SPIRITUAL BYPASSING

Sometimes, when I encounter positive-thinking theories, I want to say, "Yeah, but can we meet IRL?" I mean, I get it. Shifting your brain *can* shift the way you look at the world and this has an enormous effect on your mind and body. So it's good, right?

Yeah, until it's not.

Too many people are skipping over the bad parts of their lives, finding silver linings before they've waded through the swamp of crappy emotions that it actually takes to get there. They say, "Oh, I don't need those negative emotions in my life," and I reply, "You don't really have any choice." Shitty things happen and you will react to them. It's called being human. A lot of what I teach comes down to this simple reminder: we are here, in these bodies, having a human experience.

Human experiences are messy. Each person has their share of joys and pains, of ecstasy and heartbreak. In all the years I've sat across the table (or across the interwebs) from you, I've *never* heard anyone tell a story that doesn't include joy and pain.

So, in this book, I'm here to update positive thinking for you. To give you a method that still encompasses your life, as a messy human, in the real world. It's called the Filter Method and I developed it over years of practice and use it as part of one of my online challenges. People usually comment that it's the hardest exercise during the challenge, but also the most helpful.

I used the Filter Method for years before I gave it a name. Its principles are simple; its effect is powerful. The basic premise is: there's no such thing as the absolute truth. When things happen in our lives, we create a story about them and that's the story we react to from now until... forever. And that story we created? It's not necessarily true. In fact, it's definitely not 100% true. Because nothing ever is.

So, by taking the stories that define our lives, the ones that we tell people when we first meet them so that they understand who we are, plus some stories that are still causing us pain, and then shifting them a bit to a different truth, we dislodge those stories from our bodies and give ourselves the opportunity to replant stories that are more beneficial for us. I'll take you through the history of the Filter Method, and then the rules and steps.

The Filter Method: A History

Back in 2009, I co-owned a fertility coaching business with my bestie. It was incredibly satisfying and we had a lot of fun working together. One of the things we often discussed with our clients was the need to view a situation through a few different perspectives, in order to help emotional balance and lessen the emotional load. In the world of psychology and coaching, this is called reframing.

For years and years after, I used it in my private practice with thousands of patients, explaining to them that if they chose to look through Filter X, it would make the world look different than if they chose Filter Y. While listening to the stories that my patients and clients told, I'd often hear recurrent themes in the filters they looked through to view the world and their lives. The most common were:

"I am a victim, and everything works against me."

"I am so selfless and giving, and no one recognizes my hard work."

"I suffer unnoticed because I am too busy caring for other people."

"Everyone else has it easier than me."

"All these things happen to me because I am not good enough."

"Everyone is trying to take advantage of me."

In the room, we'd work together to replace those filters with upgraded ones, such as:

"The world is conspiring to help me."

"My input and work are appreciated and valuable."

"Other people care about me as much as I care about them."

"Everyone has their own struggle."

"My life has many positive experiences."

"Everyone is trying to help me."

And in that, the Filter Method was born! The how-to is simple, so let's jump right in.

Six Rules of The Filter Method

The first rule of the Filter Method is: never use it on a fresh issue

I mean this, folks. This method is to be applied to old wounds and beliefs that you are hanging on to like a dog with a bone. The crappy stories that you keep repeating need to be dug up from the backyard and shifted for good. The current problems? Learn to sit in the muck. (That's another class.)

The second rule of the Filter Method is: choose one issue at a time

Do not, I repeat, *do not* try to fix multiple problems at one time. Once you get the hang of this, you'll be using the Filter Method all the time without even planning on it... because it's fun and powerful and you can do it anywhere. Until then, stick to one issue, one story. Don't make it more than your burnt-out brain can handle.

The third rule of the Filter Method is: spare your friends the details

It is common, when you find something this good, to want to tell the world about it. It's called neophyte status and I love to see it in your eyes. You get excited at this helpful thing. It's soooo helpful and you want to help everyone! Your friends, though? If they haven't made the decision to work through their crap, they literally *do not want to hear* about how you have. It'll push them to defend their issues and solidify those issues in their lives. You really want to help them? Suggest this book on social media! If they're meant to find it, they will. And you'll be helping me spread the word at the same time!

The fourth rule of the Filter Method is: accept there are multiple truths

In order for this to be a successful method for you, you need to embrace that there are, at a minimum, three sides to every story – yours, your counterparty's, and the bird's eye objective view. I'd argue that there are infinite versions of every story, but for now, let's agree that there are at least three. The emotions that you carry about the story that you're telling are based on the version of the story that you decided was true. This means that your emotional reactions to old stories and situations are a choice and can be changed.

The fifth rule of the Filter Method is: none of the filters is an *absolute* truth

In order for me to maintain my promise that this is positive thinking upgraded, I need you to really take note of this fifth rule. Once you hear a filter that you like, it can be easy to hold onto it for dear life and never let it go. You want so badly for this filter to be true, that you forget the fifth rule and fly away into the sunset with your filter of choice. This isn't healthy. It is important to be able to use various filters, which are useful for reminding you of the fourth rule: that there are multiple truths and that how you are reacting in any situation relates directly to a truth you *chose*.

The sixth rule of the Filter Method is: your filter, your choice

Recognize that you are choosing to use a particular filter and that it is no more true than any other filter. If you're looking at your life and feeling like shit, change your filter. Your filter, your choice. Until this very moment, perhaps this sixth rule wasn't true for you. Your filters were 'gifted' to you by your elders in the magical time between birth and age six. You might have gotten some really crappy filters handed down to you, so no blaming yourself here. It's simply time to take responsibility for changing them. Also, another word on blame: it's not your elders' fault either. They were stuck with their own filters before they passed them onto you.

The filters through which you ultimately choose to view the world are responsible for how satisfied you are with life. This sixth rule is one that I want you to apply to other people as well. When you're using the Filter Method, it's easy to want other people to change their filters so that they feel better, but here's the thing: their filter, their choice. Usually, we choose filters because they protect us in some way: either they protect our ego, or they pretend to protect us from pain. If someone is not ready to look at their stories and shift them, don't force it. In fact, if you've read through these rules and feel some hesitance, come back to it another time.

The Filter Method increases bouncebackability by factors of 100 at a time because it releases *so much* stuck energy that can be used for better things, but you need to be ready to start using it and feel safe. If you need to, I encourage you to take this exercise and work it through with a coach or counselor.

Now that you know the rules, here is how you use the Filter Method. There are 10 steps set up in an easy-to-follow format. I suggest you pull out your journal right away. You're going to want to get started on this A.S.A.P.

The 10 Steps of The Filter Method

Step 1: Choose a story that you tell others about your life that has a negative connotation.

I know I've held onto stories about my in-laws for ages. I decided they were a certain way and that explained my feelings for them. I was in the right, according to my story, and it made space for my emotional reactions. In order to justify how I felt, I'd tell people the stories that were the most shocking, usually with some humor thrown in because that's my style.

I'd tell the story, for instance, about how my mother-in-law took a shawl off my shoulders while I was at a wedding and hid it from me because, according to her, I should 'show off my chest'. I mean, this is clearly abnormal behavior and crosses all sorts of boundaries, but I latched onto the story as my justification for my emotions (reminder: you don't *need* justification for your emotions

– they're usually not logical anyway). At some point, it stopped being healthy to hold on and I had to change the filter.

The best story to choose to work on is a situation where you feel like you were wronged, where the feelings that you have about it toward the other person are lingering, and where someone is *obviously* (in your mind) to blame. It might be them or it might be you. Either is valid for the sake of the exercise.

Most often, this is a story that you'd tell someone new-ish in your life to 'explain' your behavior in a particular circumstance. For instance, if you were cheated on, you might tell this to your new friends to explain why you're checking your phone for a text from your partner for the thousandth time. Or maybe you'll say that you raised yourself and that's why you're so independent. I'd tell the shawl story to people to explain why I was stressed out to travel to my in-laws' home for the holidays.

Step 2: Write out the story related to the issue.

You must write or type your story. Thinking through it isn't enough. Write the story the way you tell it to a friend, emphasizing the things that went wrong and how wrong this person was to hurt you or how at fault you were. Write is as if you were sharing it with someone who hadn't heard it yet and you were trying to convince them of the correctness of your emotional reaction to it.

Really take the time to write it all out. When I did this, it was both cathartic and disturbing. I'd allowed all the good things my mother-in-law does to be overshadowed by her faults.

Step 3: Read your story out loud and listen for a belief that is hidden in it.

Really, out loud. Reading stories out loud is amazingly powerful and allows us a vantage point that we just don't have when the story is simple in our heads. Reading it out loud from a written version gives us two degrees of separation and makes it way easier to listen with the ears of an observer. Listen for repeating themes like: I am not good enough, I never get support, I'm always last picked, people don't pay attention to me, everyone is an idiot, no one listens, people are assholes....

When I read mine out loud, the belief was: I am a good person and my in-laws are disrespectful.

Step 4: Write out the belief at the bottom of the story.

Just jot it down in its full form. If you feel moved to write more proof about why it's true, throw it down on that paper too. Create distance. Become the observer.

Step 5: Reword the belief into something more positive.

You'll need a good ol' switcheroo here. If your belief was "everyone is an idiot," you can try replacing it with "people are doing the best they can with what they have." If your belief was "I never get support," you can replace it with, "the universe has my back" (thanks for this one, Gabby Bernstein). If you are having a hard time with this, try looking at your belief and answering the question: what is the opposite of this belief?

For me, in this scenario, it was a shift from "I'm a good person and my in-laws are disrespectful" to "I have both positive and negative aspects about me, just like everyone else. Cultural differences between us mean the boundaries that are normal for me aren't necessarily normal and clear to them."

Step 6: Write the new belief at the top of a new page.

New story, new page. Having a new page literally gives you a clean slate. Start with this new belief. Write it on the top of a fresh page, then close your eyes and feel it in your body. Find even a small percentage of truth in this new filter, this new belief. Maybe your shoulders will relax, maybe you'll sigh loudly, maybe you'll feel the truth of it in your gut. You also might notice some resistance. At the very least, you're looking for some rising curiosity that leads you to want to rewrite the story and see how it turns out.

Step 7: Rewrite your story, through the filter of this new belief.

Pretend that the new belief is totally true. Write down your story from this new perspective. If this belief was *the truth*, what would this change about this situation? How would your emotions shift? You'll *feel* your emotions changing as you write the new story. And you'll fight them. But keep going anyway.

[WARNING: Do *not* make the story beautiful if it's shitty by nature. Shifting the filter does not shift the actual *events* of the story. It shifts the *feelings* and *emotions* that we attached to the story after the fact. For instance, if you story includes being bullied and your filter was "everyone is out to get me" and your new filter is "there is support in other people," that doesn't mean that the bullying never happened. The new story should be just as much the truth as the old story – just a different version. Do not sugarcoat toxic scenarios. Do not silver-lining shit that was bad. If you were abused, that's still a *fact* of the story. Include it. This version shouldn't be rainbows and unicorns, but a slight perspective shift.]

In my example, the new story goes like this: *I was at a wedding and my mother-in-law removed my shawl. I noticed then that we had a difference in what boundaries and personal space meant. Since that time, I never made an effort to make my boundaries known because I felt uncomfortable and like it would be disrespectful, so she never knew how much what she did bothered me. I didn't give her a chance to shift behavior. Instead, I held onto past hurts and used them for judgment. In the future, I can choose to make my feelings clear with as much respect as possible and allow space for change. If there is no change after I make the request, I can choose what I would like to do with the relationship. The boundaries are up to me.*

131

Step 8: Ego check yourself before you wreck yourself.

You're gonna fight this, I promise. Your ego wants to be right and is always searching for information that corroborates its beliefs. So, you'll be writing the second story thinking, *This is bullshit. This isn't true. My story is true! My feelings are right!*

Yeah, I know, I've done it too... Just tell your ego to slow its roll and play along for a little while longer. It's hard to separate ourselves from our convictions, especially when they boil down to one of two things:

1. Somebody wronged me;

2. I'm guilty of wronging someone else.

Both of these things can be true *and* how you feel about the story can shift. I know for an absolute fact that you've already changed stories like this in your life without knowing what the Filter Method was. It happened when you were furious at a friend for not calling you back and then you found out that their parent was rushed to the hospital. It happened when you were hurt by something your spouse said but when you talked it through with your bestie, you realized it was more than likely not directed at you. It's a natural thing that we do. Unless there is a trauma. Then we get stuck on repeat and hold on for dear life.

Step 9: Repeat with two more filters until you have at least four true versions of your story.

As you try on more and more filters, your ego will start to back down because it realizes you're just messing around with the story and seeing what's possible. You aren't forcing it to change. Play with this. Try a few different filters. If your original was "everyone's an idiot" and your first filter was "people are doing the best they can with what they have," the second one could be "every individual has a different rule book they live by." The third, "everyone I meet has their own set of pain and struggles."

The more versions of this story you write, the more the grips of the emotional trauma attached to it will loosen. Who knows... Maybe you'll let go of the original version that has been causing you pain altogether. (But that's not necessarily the goal.)

Another filter on mine could be (and this one is *hard* for me to write, and makes me want to say, "But my truth is TRUUUUUUEEEE!"): "my mother-in-law always wants what is best for me and she sees beauty in me that she is proud of." The story would sound like: *I was at a wedding and my mother-in-law took off my shawl and hid it so that I couldn't put it back on. She said it was because I should show off my chest and shoulders. She is always so proud of the way I look. I was upset when she did it, but I know how important it is for her that we are noticed and appreciated.*

Step 10: Choose the filter that created the story you like best and agree to make this the updated version of your story.

That's it. You've updated your story. Now, every time you find yourself ready to repeat your old story, correct yourself and slide in your new story. Allow the more comfortable emotions associated with it to sink into your brain and reduce your inner stress levels, increasing your bouncebackability factor.

When you change stories that were stuck in blame, you increase your bouncebackability bandwidth because you recognize that you've been through something difficult and uncomfortable, and made it through the other side. Maybe the situation has even improved afterwards. You start to see yourself in a different light and that increases your self-worth and internal power.

That's it. Ten simple but profound steps. You can repeat this process as often as you want with *any* situation in your life.

Remember the rules. This method is *not* to be used to spiritually bypass a set of emotions that are fresh and need time to process. If you're supposed to be sitting in the muck, sit in the damn muck. This method is to be used for old garbage that you are still carrying around that isn't helping you in any way at all whatsoever, and in fact might be stopping you from living the life you want to live.

When your energy is tied up in emotional reactions to old stories and scenarios, you deplete your own bouncebackability. It's like a rubber band: if you stretch it, it's resilient and it'll bounce back and take its first form, but if it was already stretched and you pull it further, at some point it will snap. And if you're burnt out, *you've already snapped*. The stories that exist in your brain and body are the ones that kept your elastic already slightly overstretched all the time. Clear them out, regain your bouncebackability, and take back your energy and your power.

When you take the time to clear out your old stories one by one, you'll create a new habit and it will become second nature to use the Filter Method subconsciously. At this point, you'll be able to bounce back more easily with newer, more current situations, because you'll view them differently, your emotional reaction will be different, and most likely you'll find those feelings easier to handle.

I believe in clarity and everything always makes more sense to me when I see it in action, so here's another worked-through example.

Original Story: (I have actually told people this story, for instance a professional photographer who I hired for some brand photos.) I have a funny-looking laugh. When I laugh, my bottom teeth go in drastically and make me look like I have an amazing overbite. I was teased for it growing up and even into college. I often used to hide my mouth when I laughed because I was embarrassed. I didn't smile much in pictures because the bigger the smile, the greater the likelihood I'd look stupid and unappealing. I'm so embarrassed by my smile that I'm never sure how to act in pictures.

Filter: "If I don't look perfect, I won't be accepted."

New Filter: "I am good enough just as I am."

Updated Version: I love to laugh. It changes my whole face when I laugh a laughter that is deep and true. The people I am with can feel the shift in my energy when something really tickles me. I use laughter as part of my teachings and I laugh every day with my patients. I used to be embarrassed by my laugh because of what my face looked like. I realized after some time that I enjoyed laughter so much that it was worth the risk of a sideways glance. Allowing myself to be in the moment and feel the joy without inhibition has been one of the greatest gifts I have given myself.

Now, I laugh with abandon. When I find myself holding back because I'm feeling self-conscious, I work to tell this new story. Right now in my life, I've embodied the second version of this story about 90%. There are still moments when it gets me, but it's not constant and it takes up *way* less space in my life and *way* less energy overall.

Both of these stories are true. The top story was one that I carried with me even into my marriage. I nearly had a fight with my husband one day because I thought he was making fun of me. My fear, my filter, made me see his reaction in a different light than it was intended. When I told him about it, he was astounded that I ever felt this way and he sat with me and said, "But you're so beautiful when you laugh." This filter of mine was so strong within me that I didn't believe him when he said this. That's when I knew I needed to work on it.

Your filters are powerful and can change your relationships and interactions with people because you taint every word, every action, every interaction. If you put an "I'm not pretty enough" spin on every interaction you have, you'll find the 'evidence' to back up that belief even if it isn't there.

Shift your thinking toward the positive. Leave space for the moments where you need to sit in the muck. Change out your filters where necessary and free yourself from the gremlins that live inside your head.

No More Spiritual Bypassing

As I mentioned earlier, spiritual bypassing is a method of avoiding emotions that is often used by those who choose to live a 'spiritual' or 'positive vibes only' life. Most often, it helps them avoid feelings of anger and other emotions that they deem 'negative'. Let's just set that straight real quick. There *are* no damn negative emotions. The only emotions that have an overall negative effect on your body are those that are pushed away and ignored. Richard Rohr, a Franciscan friar, gave humanity this quote which I adore: "Pain which is not transformed is transferred".

Each emotion, in and of itself, is natural. Chinese medicine has said for millennia that the only harmful emotions are the stuck unprocessed ones. In Chinese medicine, each organ has an emotion associated with it. These emotions, when felt and processed, give the organ a boost. Just like a good stress response gives the immune system a boost. When stuck, these emotions are said to damage the organ that they belong to.

If you are interested in exploring this further, the emotional-organ chart below is a starting point for you to see which emotions are stored where in the body:

Joy/Mania	Heart
Anger	Liver

Grief/Sadness	Lungs
Fear	Kidneys
Worry	Spleen

But how do you process emotions? If you were never taught to do this, it can seem like an insurmountable task. If that's the case, the first thing you should do is see a therapist. Qualified professionals exist to help you in this exact area of life. It is possible that they will suggest medication, which, when necessary, can feel like an angel packaged up in a pill. There are some filters and brain changes that need the help of a pill to reinstate plasticity and, like everything else in this book, should have *no shame* attached to it.

If you need respite from the programs that you were given as a child, following a trauma, or for any other reason, get the help you need first. Then, work on the rest.

CHAPTER 16

TACKLING BURNOUT REASON #3 OTHER PEOPLE'S TEMPLATES

Changing your family (or cultural) templates becomes easy once you've done the Filter Method because the system is similar. The main difference to me is that other people's templates are *rules of life* that you follow, not filters that you use to view situations. The similarity is that you decided they were correct at some point and they are wasting your energy.

I mentioned earlier what your templates might look like. Let's dig into that further. A life template, according to yours truly, is a set of life rules that you were taught were correct and you follow without question even if they don't sit well with you. These templates impede your bouncebackability factor because you spend your time judging yourself against where you are based on where other people think you should be. And because people constantly ask you where you are according to your family's or your culture's template. Say you have two MDs as your parents – the whole world wants to know when you're going to medical school but you want to be a chef. It's a mess and takes up loads of energy that could be used differently.

I was talking to a nurse today who told me that – *gasp!* – she was turning 30 in nine months and she was already freaked out about it because she's not married and doesn't have any kids and doesn't own a house; she hasn't ticked off any of the boxes that she 'should' have ticked off by this point. *Oof.* Sister. Come sit with me. Those boxes shouldn't even exist anymore. Life isn't designed the way it used to be. We are taught growing up that there are things you need to do to be happy. Own a home. Have a 'secure' job. Have a family. Every family places more weight on some things than others. And they're all wrong. There's no list of outside accomplishments or check boxes that will make you happy. Feelings of happiness are difficult to find at all when you're trying to check off those boxes. Feelings of burnout are easy to find there.

For us as entrepreneurs, we are usually breaking quite a few molds. Staying home as full-time mothers and owning businesses? We're making it work. Creating careers for ourselves that might not look stable on the outside but bring us joy? We're doing that. Learning to invest our own money instead of keeping that job we hated with a 401K? Yep, we're breaking that mold too. Spending money on courses that enrich our lives when we don't know what the payout will be? Yep, add that to the list of shit we do that makes our families uncomfortable. Creating businesses based on stuff that didn't exist 10 years ago? Uh huh, we're going there.

So, we're already changing templates. Do we really need an exercise to do it some more? Yes! Wanna know why? Because we're breaking those templates and often still feeling guilty about it. We're holding onto old energy and other people's expectations that we've already proven we don't want to hold ourselves to, so we carry both the old and the new and then wonder why we're tired.

This is something I spend a lot of time on with clients when working one on one. I'll give you an example.

My natural tendency is to be the center of attention. I like entertaining people, I like making people laugh, I like telling good stories. My mother, who is my favorite person and a huge influence

139

on my life, does not like being the center of attention at all. She's always described herself as plain and she doesn't ever wear anything that will garner attention. Clothes should be functional, utilitarian in nature, maybe a little cute, but not too flashy.

In response to this, my sister went flashy. I'm talking full make-up (she's a genius at it), hair done, great clothes, always with an amazing pair of shoes. I, on the other hand, was never sure what to do. I want to be noticed for my storytelling, my wit, not my appearance. I thought I would be valued more if I looked 'natural' – like I wasn't trying. One of my friends, a big-time personal stylist in Poland, once told me that I had a lot of work to do in the style department and asked why none of my profile pictures were ever pretty. *Ouch.*

The truth is that even though I like to be the center of attention and entertain people, because it was against my mother's template, I thought it was against mine too. My besties got me a photoshoot for my birthday a few years back because they told me I needed to learn to be comfortable in front of the camera. It was *so* hard for me back then, but I'll admit that I really love it now! Blending in and not being noticed was a template that I had inherited from my family, but it's not *my* nature!

Rebuilding this template has taken me nearly a decade. I have an amazing pair of glasses that I'm obsessed with, a few dresses that'll knock your socks off, and I love getting professional photos done. I can now easily make a Pinterest board of styles I like and feel like it's okay for me to wear them in real life. When I started rehashing this part of my life, the things I chose on Pinterest where the safe things I had always chosen. Simple jeans, t shirts, practical everyday dresses that are workable even if they aren't great. It still takes a little courage for me to buy the thing I *really* want vs. the thing that will get the most use and be the most practical. I was one of those people who bought jeans just because they fit, not because they were flattering. Now, I try to make sure they do both.

I like working with people on their templates because once they find and expand upon the ones that are truly theirs, they feel *so comfortable* and it makes so much sense that living any other way was costing *way* more energy than it was worth. Some common templates I see are:

1. Winning is everything. It's always a competition. This one makes sense for people who like to compete, but often, people are raised by parents who like to compete even though they don't like it. We need competitors. I love watching sports. Competition is *fun*, when it's amongst people who are meant to compete. If that's not you but it was, for instance, your dad, you might be draining all of your energy by competing.

2. What will other people think? This wasn't my household, but in Poland it's really common. I don't believe we can honestly say we don't care at all what people think. On some level, it tends to matter to us no matter who we are or how we were brought up. However, if your mother never left the house without makeup and her hair done, you might be doing the same without stopping to ask if it's fitting and necessary for you. Is this in your nature or is it inherited? Is it boosting your energy or draining it?

3. You're in a 'safe' job because it will 'always' exist. *Welp.* We all know that's becoming less and less true. So many of us followed our parents' life choices when it comes to comfort and risk. How many people became teachers because it was safe, they'd have summers off, etc.? Talk about burnout… All-time records among teachers! Even if you're called to be a teacher, you can burn out; never mind if you chose it because it was 'safe'. My bestie ended up being a tax advisor because her father valued math over all things. She hates math. Now, she's a high-level business coach and spiritual mentor, and *way* happier.

141

4. Finish high school. Finish college. Get a job. Get married. Have kids. I know, I know. This template isn't just your family; it's life at large. But is it yours? I'm so grateful I took time to travel, and soooo grateful that my husband and I stopped to think about what we wanted life to look and feel like before making a decision about children. You're told that if you follow this template, you'll be happy. But guess what. For a lot of us, it's not working. Living the life less common is risky and difficult because it's harder to believe it can 'work'. But if you've never been satisfied with the status quo (that's me, folks... always seeking, searching, looking, learning...), this template probably doesn't belong to you.

5. Your job as a woman is to take care of other people first. The caretaker role often falls on women and it's been the template of many a society for millennia. Again, is it yours though? This is a big one. Not everyone wants to 'mother' as a verb even if they want to be mothers. We are living in a time of choice and change. If you're not naturally a nurturer, don't pretend. It'll burn you out and breed resentment. If this is your template, *great*! If it's not, *great*! Just be sure you're doing you.

6. Your role as a man is to provide financial stability. The flip side of the female nurturer template is this assumption that men provide the money. But what if you're a man and a natural nurturer? Let your wife get back to the office where she shines and use your skills where they serve and feel best to you. Templates aren't set in stone. If the one that works for your brother, father and cousin isn't yours, don't follow it.

How do you know if you're following a template (or five) that doesn't belong to you? Answer these questions with a yes or a no:

Are you doing 'all the right things' but still burning out?

Do you feel resentful about doing things you think you 'should' do?

Do you often use the words: 'must', 'should', or 'have to'?

Do things that look effortless to others feel burdensome to you?

Do you often stop and think: is this it?!?!

Do you judge people for doing something differently, even though you feel a little jealous?

Are you doing most things on autopilot?

Will you just scream if you have to (x) again?

Do you often question if you had a good time when everyone else claims it was a nice day?

Do you find yourself shifting decision-making to someone else even when you know what your decision would be should you be allowed to make it alone?

Shifting Other People's Templates

If you answered yes to three or more of the above, you've got a few templates that need shifting! But how do you do it? Great question. The first thing, as always, is *noticing*. Start keeping notes, whether that's in a journal or the notes app in your phone. Notice what makes you sigh. Notice when you feel resentment and burden. Notice when you feel like you are efforting more than is necessary. For a whole week, without changing anything, write those moments down.

After seven days, take a look at your list. Put check marks next to the habits you never questioned that you inherited from parents, caregivers or teachers.

Next, take the one that seems to repeat most on the list and make a commitment to watch it over the next week. How often do you use it? When is it helpful? When is it harmful? After looking at one template for a few weeks, you should be able to answer whether or not you see the value in this particular way of being. If you don't, it's time to create a new one!

Creating a new template is simple. You take the template that you decided wasn't working for you and you choose something better. So, for instance, if the template you decided is wearing you down sounds like "I'm responsible for everyone's wellbeing," you choose a new template by flipping that one on its head. It might now sound like "I'm responsible for my own wellbeing and everyone else is responsible for theirs."

This new template becomes a mantra. You say it over and over and over and over until it creates one of those brain grooves. It's not an excuse to be a jerk. It's a reminder to yourself to mind your own energy and allow other people to mind theirs (in this particular example). You can say to yourself, "I choose to do this differently. I choose to put myself high on my list of priorities and care for my wellbeing in all situations".

If you find yourself having a hard time with this (changing templates is one of those simple but not easy things), my suggestion is to make a God Box. If you're not into god, you can call it a Help Me Box, or a Universe Box, it works no matter what you call it.

I was introduced to this concept in the book *Outrageous Openness* by Tosha Silver, which is my most recommended book of all time. The idea behind a God Box is simple: when you have a situation that you either don't have any control over or aren't sure how to shift it yourself, you write it down and put it in the box. Once it's in the box, you agree to let God (or the Universe, or your Ancestors) take over. When you're making a new template, your entry to your God Box might sound like, "Please help me make this shift to caring more for my own wellbeing with support and ease." Write it down, put it in the box. Let the magic do its work.

As time passes with template work, you will notice that you are shifting them with minimal effort. A new one will pop up that you hadn't noticed before and you'll go through this whole process without much thought. As soon as you allow them to come to the surface, they will come with glee, cheering, "Change me! Shift me! I don't belong to you anymore!" It's an incredibly empowering thing to do for yourself and helps you create life (and business!) on your own terms.

CHAPTER 17

TACKLING BURNOUT REASON #4
HONESTY

Getting honest with yourself and living a bullshit-free existence clears so many damn avenues, it should be a whole book. In fact, there are whole books about it. In the book *Radical Honesty: How to Transform Your Life By Telling The Truth*, author Brad Blanton writes, "It's not normal to be honest. What is normal is to be concerned foremost with having a good cover story. Normal people are concerned with figuring out the right thing to say that puts them in the best light. They want to live up to their own best guess about what the people they are talking to want to hear."

Being honest about who you are and what you want is *hard*. It seems like the simplest thing in the world, but we all lie... All. The. Time. Especially in the world of social media, we most often lie by omission. Even our 'vulnerable' moments are shared with a positive twist that has some goal attached to it. In an interview, I heard Brené Brown call that 'fauxnerability' and I totally agree.

I'm not asking you here to bare your soul to the world and let everyone in on your secrets. I'm not even asking you for the type of radical honesty that Blanton writes about in his book. I'm asking you to stop bullshitting yourself. I'm asking you to at least trust yourself enough with your truth, even if you don't do anything about it. Maintaining internal lies is a huge energy suck and it drains your bouncebackability. It's hard to bounce back when the shape you should be returning to is a lie.

So, what's the exercise for this one? It all starts with one word: *fine*. This is another topic that a whole book has been written about. The Mel Robbins book I mentioned earlier – *Stop Saying You're Fine: Discover a More Powerful You* – is full of truths on this subject. For the short version and to get you working toward getting more honest with yourself, here is the gist:

Anything that you say is 'fine' = bullshit.

If you haven't gotten a journal to go with this book yet, you should probably get one now, because there's a lot of writing that happens when you're bouncing back from burnout; it's one of the only real ways to create perspective, clear your mind, and transform emotions all at once. What I want you to do is a bastardized version of proprioceptive writing, a technique created and taught by Linda Trichter Metcalf who discovered it in the 1970s when she was a professor at Pratt in New York City. I highly recommend, when you've got more energy, reading her book *Writing the Mind Alive* and practicing the real version of proprioceptive writing, but here, because you're burnt out, I'll keep it simple.

Grab your trusty bouncebackability journal and write 'fine' at the top of a fresh page. Under the word 'fine', I want you to note down every time you say that you or something else is fine for a whole week. That's right, a *whole week*. Keep this notebook by your side, as she's gonna need to come out quite a bit. Then, at the end of the week, take three examples from your list and answer this question: What did I mean by 'fine' in this situation?

I'll give you an example. You're out to dinner and you've ordered salmon with veggies and rice. Your partner asks how it is. You say it's fine. So, you write in your journal: I said the salmon at

147

Murray's Restaurant was fine. Later that week, reflect on that statement with the question: when I said the salmon was fine at Murray's, what did I really mean? And then be as *honest* as possible. It might look like this: what I meant was, I didn't order the meal that I wanted because I'm afraid I'm gaining weight, so I ordered something 'healthy'. It was enjoyable enough but it could have used a little more flavor, and really, I wanted some ribs. When I said it was fine, what was actually true for me in that moment was: this salmon is disappointing, not because it's bad but because I'm forcing myself to order and eat it for the wrong reasons.

This exercise, for me, is fun. I love getting honest with myself because it makes me so much more colorful and enjoyable as a person. If I was sitting in Murray's with my husband in that scenario, now I would admit I ordered the salmon because it was the healthier choice, but I'd rather have ribs. And we'd probably both laugh. The more you practice being honest about small things like this, the easier it is for you to be honest about the big things when they come up.

Everything in life requires practice. You don't read this book, decide on honesty, and then head out into the world shouting everything that you think is true into the streets. You practice honesty in small bits and pieces, ones that don't feel so scary, so that when you're faced with a moment where your honest opinion will make a major impact on your life, you know how to find your voice – even if you disappoint someone.

When you're honest, you're able to admit when your business isn't going the way you wanted it to. You're able to admit when you're wasting time on a new website because you're afraid of making sales. You're able to admit that you loved this idea 10 years ago but you've grown out of it now and it's time to start something new – even if it means starting from scratch – *again*. You burn out and destroy your bouncebackability factor when you stick to things

148

too long that don't belong to you or match you anymore. It's soul-sucking to maintain a business because it looks good on the outside or you've reached a level of financial security that makes people say, "But you've got it all!"

Getting to the place where you're able to be honest about the big stuff means practicing with the small stuff. It means focusing on the word 'fine' and figuring out what you really mean when you say it. As a bonus, if this exercise feels easy and fun for you, you can move from *fine* to the next level words: *busy, stressed,* or *fat.* During a podcast episode with Teri Hofford, a body positive activist and photographer, we talked about a blog post of hers where she asks people to stop saying "I feel fat" because fat isn't an emotion! She asks people to pay attention when they say this and then figure out what they are actually feeling. What do they really mean when they say, "I feel fat." Do they feel physically bloated? Are they feeling undesirable? Are they depressed? What do they mean?

At the end of the day, you can use this with any word and that's the basis behind proprioceptive writing and its famous question: what do I mean by.......? It changes your whole world when you take time to dig under the surface. There's a whole burnt-out entrepreneur under there who has been begging for your attention and can't wait to get her voice heard. Break out that journal and let her sing!

CHAPTER 18

TACKLING BURNOUT REASON #5 ENVIRONMENT

If you're not an entrepreneur, changing your environment often means quitting your job. There are job environments that lend themselves to burnout more than others because of terrible fluorescent lights and micromanaging bosses with tuna breath. Burnout is proven to occur more when we have: less autonomy, less flexibility, and less support. So, if you're reading this book as an employee and your job sucks, time to get a new one!

When you're an entrepreneur, it's not so straightforward. Sure, you could go out and get a job, but we can also work on shifting your environment to make it better. If autonomy, creativity, flexibility, and support are things you need, we can figure out how to add them. When I did Marie Forleo's B-School, an online business school course that teaches you how to create (according to her tagline!) a business and life you love, Marie started the program by making a war cry to participants. When we were focusing on this program, we were meant to focus. That might mean putting a 'do not disturb' sign on the door or simply sticking to the dedicated time you've given yourself. I can hear the collective of mothers groaning at this point telling me it's impossible, but here's the thing... it's not.

There's science that tells us that it takes us 23 minutes to get back to the task at hand when our concentration is disturbed – even if it's just a ping from a text message that we don't even read. So, even if it's impossible because you're a stay-at-home mother in addition to an entrepreneur, what you can do is limit the distractions as much as possible. Airplane mode yourself so that your only disruptions come from your kids, even if just for 10 minutes at a time.

The ritual of shutting yourself off from the buzzes, dings, and rings of the world is an amazing way to let your brain and body know it's time to focus. The more you're able to focus, the less you'll burn out. We often don't realize how many distractions we have until we start to eliminate them one by one. As entrepreneurs, we need to eliminate as many as possible! Focusing creates feelings of control and autonomy because we're across our shit, and we know what we need and when we need it. When we're unable to focus (common for the burnt-out among us who are foggy-headed), we feel like we have no autonomy whether or not that's actually true.

In addition to creating better boundaries around our working-from-home-or-a-coffee-shop environment, we can improve the space in which we work simply by getting a nicer lamp, by adding a blue light blocking screen to our computers (helps to manage the damage from all that screen-staring!), by getting flowers, by changing the artwork, or by reorganizing the furniture. I'm not an interior designer or a Feng Shui expert, but if you need either of those things to create a space for yourself, go do it!

Another great trick for those of us who work at home is to have a ritual to start your 'working' times. It is so easy to let our work hours spill into life hours and vice versa, because they are so intertwined when you are at home. Yet, by creating a ritual before you start working, you are setting a tone, creating a boundary, and letting your body and brain know where they are and how you want them to be performing.

My ritual looks like this: I straighten the kitchen (it's a thing), and then I go into my office and light a candle or incense. I sit down at my desk and take three deep breaths. I work with affirmations and I have a dog-headed Buddha on my desk, so I take a moment to say thank you and repeat my affirmations and then I get to work. When it's time for a break, I say thank you, stand up, and stretch before moving on to doing the laundry or whatever task I'll do to create a mindless moment in my day where information percolates in my brain because my body is engaged in something mundane. I love those moments because they often allow me to come up with creative solutions to problems. I call this 'creating brain space'. Thinking isn't always the best option!

Feeling good in the space that you are working, knowing that you have periods where you will not be disturbed, and having rituals in place that signify to you, your body, and your brain that you are entering and leaving work mode will allow you to focus more, be more productive and burn out less.

CHAPTER 19

TACKLING BURNOUT REASON #6 BOUNDARIES

Ah, my favorite topic: the Knot. I've waited almost the whole book to share this with you. If the Filter Method is positive thinking upgraded, then the Knot is boundary-building updated. In the earlier chapter on boundaries, I mentioned something that I like to call your 'inner boundary'. Remember that thing where you don't jump into other people's lives and problems uninvited? Boundaries are more about not overstepping, than about being assertive. Assertiveness training is about creating boundaries for the outside coming in, whereas the Knot is about creating boundaries for *you* going out.

The Knot Theory

Imagine for a second that there is a net that covers the earth and connects us all to one another. Look up and you'll see that above you, there is a knot. This knot belongs to you. It is yours to take care of, to look after. You do so by fulfilling your destiny, by living in alignment, and by building and keeping your energy in your space. You have one job while you are here on earth and maintaining your knot is it. It is not your job to fix your neighbor's knot. It is not your job to look around and judge how other knots are holding up.

If you stop and focus on what your knot is doing, you are contributing in exactly the way you are supposed to. Your sole (soul?) focus is maintaining the integrity of *your knot*. And it is by doing this, I repeat, *by doing this* that you make the job easier on the people around you to maintain their knots. Not by helping them directly, but by focusing on yourself and your knot.

When you have what I like to call 'Good Person syndrome', also known as being a people-pleaser, it's hard for you to focus on your own knot. One of the biggest hindrances in taking care of your own knot is the fact that you are constantly assessing and anticipating other people's needs (OPNs) even before they know they have them. As a Good Person in the world, this is a conundrum, because you like to be considerate, you want to be a nice person, and you work hard at doing that. You even pride yourself on it.

Here are the problems with that:

1. You're fixing things for other people that they are often perfectly capable of fixing themselves.

2. You're fixing things for people that they never wanted fixed in the first place.

3. You *think* you're fixing something, but really you're just being annoying.

When you do this, you are messing up your own energy a few ways:

1. You are abandoning your own needs. You are so focused on OPNs that you fail to realize that you are tired, hungry, need to pee, need a hug, etc., until it's too late. Abandoning your own needs means that you aren't caring for your own knot and it's loosening,

unraveling, and getting frayed, because you aren't there to notice and react.

2. You are telling the people around you that you don't trust them and don't believe they are capable of handling their own lives (knots). You know better, you know how to do it easier, it'll be faster if you just do it yourself. This is rude and it breaks down other people's self-awareness and self-confidence. How are they able to survive without you? Believe me, if given the chance, they'll do just fine. Maybe different from how you imagine it, but that's okay too.

3. You are sending your focus and attention outside of yourself into what you assume other people might want and need, and therefore have less of your own energy available to use. Guess what the biggest symptom of this is. Fatigue! If you're sick of saying that you're tired, it's time to refocus on *your knot*!

These three things – all three of them – affect your bouncebackability and burn you out. When you abandon yourself, you ignore the simple aspects of self-care because you're more concerned with making someone else comfortable than you are with getting a healthy lunch in or brushing your teeth. When you are constantly in other people's space, upgrading the lives of those around you that they don't want upgrading, you're burning oil! This is a direct burnout issue. As entrepreneurs, especially those in coaching or any type of healing, we often start out our careers wanting more for people than they want for themselves. All that energy we spend trying to get them to where we want them to be but is beyond where they have decided they need to be? It's wasted.

When you are not able to keep enough of your own energy in your own space, you lose track of what you want, need, and desire. You're unable, after a time, to even rebuild your energy because you lose touch with how and you regenerate. You don't know what color throw pillows you want. (What might your family like?) You

155

can't choose a restaurant because you're more concerned with everyone else eating what they like. (What about what *you* want?) It's hard to even know what that is when your energy isn't at home in your body.

Clues you're not taking care of your own knot:

1. *You go into fixing mode quickly.*

2. *You feel resentful when people don't take your advice.*

3. *When asked what you want in a given moment, you aren't sure how to answer.*

4. *You offer a compromise in situations when no one has asked for one.*

What kinds of things are we fixing for other people? I'll give you an example of how badly I eff this up on a daily basis and maybe it will help you see your own moments of overstepping.

I'm obsessed with making sure old ladies have seats on the tram. This means my energy is never in my own body whenever I'm on the tram, because at every stop, I'm making sure no old ladies get on board, and if they do, that someone gets up for them. It also means that I'm judging other people for not getting up at the speed that I think they should! *Not my job!* (Unless I'm sitting in the seat that should be made available to the little old ladies.) The other thing I'm doing in this situation is basically letting that old lady know that I don't trust *her* abilities to ask someone to get up if she needs a seat.

Now tell me, why would I assume that someone who has been alive twice as long as I have and has been riding these same trams her whole life doesn't have a voice? Again, rude assumption! So, I've started trusting old ladies to speak up for themselves, even if speaking up means rolling their eyes obviously enough for me to enquire if they *want* help. I cannot tell you how many times I've made a stink asking someone to get up for an old woman and then the older woman simply says, "I'm only going one stop, sit, sit," and then I walk away trying to feel justified and righteous, but realizing that I feel like a jerk.

Here's another thing that I see women doing often: assuaging someone's anger or frustration. It could be a partner's or a friend's, but when other people are angry, I know a ton of people who go into 'fixing mode' because anger is an uncomfortable emotion and most of us don't like it. So, we try to change it, even when it's not ours. We try to change the angry person's perspective: make them laugh, change the mood, or solve the problem at hand that they are struggling with.

I know I do this. Instead of solving other people's issues for them, what I've started to do is leave the room. If I can't leave the room, I try to isolate myself energetically as much as possible so that I am not in their space.

I believe in people's ability to work through their own stuff or ask for help when they need it. Sometimes, I'll offer help, but as a question, not a solution. The difference between offering a question and a solution is this:

Would you like some help figuring this out?

As opposed to:

Here's how you should do it instead.

By giving people the opportunity to let us know if our help is wanted, we waste less energy creating escape plans in our minds for their issues and problems. If they don't want a solution, they'll say so. When they say so, get the hell outta dodge. There's nothing more annoying than someone who keeps sticking their foot in when they've been clearly told that their help is unwanted.

The question now is: how do we figure out what is our knot and what belongs to other people? This is my favorite exercise! I want you to start a Resentment Journal. Yes, resentment. Grab a notebook and start noting down all the times that you feel: resentful, annoyed, underappreciated, or happen to notice yourself being passive-aggressive. Keep track of all these various annoyances for at least one week.

Once you've got a full list, take stock. How many of these situations repeat themselves? You'll want to be looking for patterns such as: 'I'm always annoyed when I unload the dishwasher... why is this *my job*?!?' Or, 'OMG, I can't believe my friend texting me *again* in the middle of the day.... doesn't she know how busy I am?' Or even better, 'Argh! This customer asks *the most basic* questions all the damn time. Google it!'

These are your big clues that let you know that you've overhelped, overstepped, or participated in an unspoken agreement where you've agreed in action but not in word. Let's break that down. In the dishwasher example, it's likely that you naturally unload the dishwasher all the time so everyone else in the household ignores that task because it's simply always done. You've entered an unspoken agreement that you didn't agree to! It's time for a conversation about your changing expectations.

In the texting friend example, if you always text back right away, you've made yourself too available and overgiven by responding when it wasn't convenient for you. Now your friend thinks that there is no inconvenient time for you. So, she writes. And you respond. Annoyed. For all you know, she might not expect that from you. It might be an expectation that you have for yourself. (I know that responding ASAP is an expectation that I held for myself for ages). Either way, if your friend thinks that you're always available and you're mad about it, a new boundary needs putting into place!

158

And the customer example... if you have a lot of overly needy customers, you'll have to take a good look at the language you use on sales calls, the 'extra' stuff that you do for them all the time. Maybe they asked you for help once and you didn't mention that next time you'd charge them so now you feel awkward, but you're working three times more than you initially planned when you signed this contract – through no fault of theirs. It's time to create a new boundary!

Conversations about new boundaries can come at a cost or with great relief. Sometimes there will be resistance from the other side. Your family might not be thrilled that you're not on dishwasher duty anymore, but they'll get used to it! You might have a chat with your friend about not always being able to respond right away and she might tell you that she never expects it – phew, pressure's off! I once had a conversation about a contract where I was overgiving and what I was able to offer the client within our contract. I knew that the cost of the conversation might be me losing this client, but I did it anyway. It turned out that she had been feeling guilty asking for so much and was happier to increase our package price to cover the cost of her true needs.

When you're able to use your annoyances, irritations, and resentments as clues to where your boundaries might need to be adjusted, you are, with each adjusted boundary, reclaiming energy for yourself. You are no longer spending time and energy in unnecessary areas. Congrats, you're back in control!

CHAPTER 20

TACKLING BURNOUT REASON #7
UNRESOLVED TRAUMA

If trauma is a part of your story – no matter how insignificant you may think it might be – it must be addressed. Avoiding it and not admitting to trauma (because other people have it worse, for instance) keeps you repeating patterns and unable to break through issues. Trauma can prevent you from doing all the things that build bouncebackability – being honest with yourself, breaking through other people's templates, meditation, breathing exercises, diet changes, all of it is made more difficult by unprocessed trauma.

I'm not here to tell you who you should talk to or how. Everyone does this a little different. I'm also not an expert in this field. When this comes up in my acupuncture or coaching practices, I refer out. That being said, I know a number of starting points. There are so many ways to deal with trauma and it's crucial that you find that right person to work with. For most of my trauma info, I follow: @aroseylife and @brittfrank and @jamesgordonmd. They approach it totally differently. Ashley Rose is a Transformational Life Coach who uses her own life experience and helps other women transform through their own traumas. Britt Frank is a licensed social worker and trauma specialist, who focuses on trauma in her practice. James Gordon is a psychiatrist who has spent his life working with highly traumatized individuals all over the world. He is the founder of the Center for Mind-Body Medicine and author of *The Transformation – Discovering Wholeness and Healing after Trauma,* which I think the whole world should read.

Most of the practices that are difficult to perform when dealing with unprocessed trauma, especially meditation and breathing exercises, are also things that allow you to break through trauma: *if you feel safe when you do them.* Meditation for traumatized burnt-out people not only sucks but doesn't work. It needs to be broken down into smaller, safer, more digestible pieces. When you hold trauma in your body, sitting still and quieting your thoughts and focusing on your breath is scary. Most of the time, you are trying to distract yourself just to stay alive; so asking you to stop doing that is just not a great idea. In the next section, we will do what I call 'unweirding meditation'. This is important because there are a million ways to 'meditate' that can feel safe and prep your brain and body to work through trauma with whichever method or therapist you choose.

Unweirding Meditation

Meditation's effect on the brain is well-researched. Every time I read more research on meditation, I want to shout from the rooftops, "Why aren't all of you doing this!??!?!" but honestly, I get it. Meditation is the simplest thing in the world that is not easy. It requires a commitment and the ability to sit with your own emotional discomfort. Its effects are cumulative, so you must practice and practice before you feel results. In the world of immediate gratification, meditation can feel like an amazing chore. Also, as I just mentioned, if you hold trauma in your body, meditation can feel scary and unsafe.

That being said, what would happen if you took in this list of what meditation does to your brain and heart? What might be different if you could help yourself in this way? Now remind yourself that you can do it for free, every day, without leaving your house.

Meditation affects nine key brain functions:

1. Helps to combat feelings of loneliness (parietal lobe)
2. Boosts creativity and brain power (corpus callosum)
3. Decreases tendency toward depression (hippocampus)
4. Improves memory and learning (hippocampus)
5. Makes you kinder and happier (inner insula)
6. Boosts emotional intelligence (temporal parietal junction)
7. Improves stress response and decreases anxiety (amygdala)
8. Increases intelligence and health (prefrontal cortex)
9. Eliminates insomnia (pons)

Can you even stand this list?

Even though this information is fairly widespread, it is hard to convince people to meditate. There are loads of misconceptions about meditation. Here, I'll clear a couple of them up for you so that you can unweird the concept in your mind and find a way of meditating that works for you. It isn't in the scope of this book to discuss the various forms of meditation, so please trust that there is a method that will work for you if you keep looking.

The word 'meditate' comes from a Latin word *meditari*, which means 'to think, to ponder, to reflect upon'. This leads us immediately into our first problem: there is this assumption about meditation that you are not supposed to think. One of the most common complaints I hear about meditation is: "But I can't stop my thoughts!" Good news! You don't have to.

Meditation is not about 'turning off' your thoughts. This idea prevents so many people from using meditation as a form of healing because there is an assumption that says, "I'm doing it wrong." I started meditating when I was 18. It's been 19 years. I still have not managed many instances where I was completely free of thought while meditating.

It is okay to have thoughts while you are meditating. The idea is: if you are sitting quietly and practicing meditation, thoughts should be allowed to arise. Your job is to not engage with them. Notice them but let them pass. I'll give you an example:

Sandy sits down to meditate. She does three deep inhales and exhales, finds a comfortable position and – *pop!* – into her head comes this thought: *What am I going to make for dinner tonight?*

A meditator, at this point, would notice this question but not answer it. A newcomer who hasn't practiced for long, on the other hand, might think: *I have chicken in the freezer. I need to take it out. I'll make that new sauce that Nancy likes, I'll have to get it going by 4:30 so that I can remember to...*

And on and on and on.

A common teaching method is to imagine the thought that arises as a cloud in the sky, and watch it pass by with a sense of indifference, maybe a slight, *Oh, that's interesting*, but nothing more. The goal here is to allow thoughts, but not allow thoughts to become stories.

Engaging with your thoughts is totally natural and you do it *all day long* without even realizing. Preventing yourself from engaging with your thoughts is a *practice*. Meditation is not something you do; it's something you practice. You'll fail a bunch of times before you get it right, and then you'll fail a bunch more, just like anything else that you've tried to master over the course of your life.

Major problem number two is: bodily position. I cannot and probably will not ever sit in a lotus position. I can't even sit in a basic cross-legged position for more than five minutes. I do most of my meditation lying down and the remainder of it upright in a chair with my feet firmly planted on the ground and my hands on my knees.

Don't let your ability, or lack thereof, to sit in the perfect meditative posture to ruin your opportunity to practice. Practice how you can. Yoga's origins were as a pre-meditative practice. The idea of yoga was to reconnect with the self and the source of all things while simultaneously preparing the body through stretching and moving to sit for an extended period of time. If you want to sit perfectly, I recommend finding a yoga class that you like, practicing daily and following it up with some time sitting in meditation. Five minutes is a great start.

Traditionally, the goal of meditation practice was to release yourself from suffering and reach Nirvana. This state of Nirvana, or Moksha depending on the origin of the practice, was one filled with love and light. It was accompanied by a state of euphoria and an understanding that everyone and everything is connected.

This blows my mind when I look at the current research on what meditation actually does to our brains. Enough practice and this state is reachable. Now, I don't believe that your average Jane has enough time in her everyday life to practice the amount that is required to reach this state. Research has shown that 20 minutes per day is optimal and I've heard that as little as three minutes is enough to rebalance the nervous system, but cannot find the research to back it up.

I have, however, anecdotal evidence to support that just a few minutes a day is hugely beneficial. The meditation that I recommend to people who are just beginning and are afraid to 'do it wrong' is this:

Choose a calming song that you already love that lasts about three minutes. Three times a day, listen to this song – through headphones is best – and while it's playing, simply listen and focus on deep belly breathing. This gives you an automatic nine minutes per day of meditation and helps you create a pattern that your body knows how to repeat when it needs to.

Over the years, patients have told me that this method decreases the intensity of their emotional reactions and allows them the space to make wiser decisions when faced with stressful situations. All that just by breathing and listening to a song... I'll take it!

In addition to Nirvana, a long-term goal of meditation is 'becoming the observer'. This state of being able to observe life from a distance is one that allows you to avoid getting caught up in emotional shit storms. It is the ultimate filter that says: "I am not my thoughts. I am not my body. I am not what you say I am. I am merely consciousness having a human experience."

The bottom line on meditation is this: something is better than nothing. Start with three minutes of breathing, just once a day if that's all you can handle at the beginning. Know that this is enough to help you and that you will naturally increase your practice with time.

Other Suggestions for Starting Meditation

I'm just going to list some ideas here, because like I've said, there's something for you out there if you're open to finding it.

1. Insight Timer – In my view, this is the best app out there for meditative practices. There are thousands of available guided meditations and they even have a seven-day introduction to meditation course that you can start out with.

2. Headspace – Another really great app that some of my patients have had huge success with. The first 10 days are free and then there is a fee for further meditations. It is structured, has reminders, and people love Andy Puddicombe's voice.

3. Find a local mindfulness course. These are now frequently offered at yoga studios and community centers.

4. Count your exercise as meditation. If your exercise routine clears your head, it counts. Runs, hikes, swims, cross-country skiing, they all have meditative qualities.

5. Heart Rate Variability – This is the techy way towards meditation. The Heart Math Institute has created a tool to measure your HRV and an app that goes along with it that allows you to practice, improve your levels of relaxation, decrease stress load, and increase the logical powers of your brain. By using it for five minutes a day for eight weeks, you can have marked improvement in all of these areas. Their studies show that high school students have less stress anxiety and better test performance, those on mental health medications are often able to (with their doctors!) reduce their dosages, blood pressure can decrease, the stress hormone cortisol can decrease, belly fat can reduce (seriously!), and more. You can head to www.heartmath.org to learn more.

6. And finally, if you're willing to try just *one* more thing meditation-based, I highly recommend you start with *none* of the above and try this instead: yoga nidra. Yoga nidra is sometimes called a body scan or yoga sleep meditation. You may have experienced it at the end of a yoga class when your teacher told you to relax the muscles of your face, scalp, neck, shoulders, etc., all the way down to your toes. Yoga nidra is a guided meditation and is available on the Insight Timer app that I mentioned above, as well as YouTube.

The best time to do a yoga nidra is lying down in bed on your way to falling asleep. This kills two birds with one stone: it gets in a daily meditation and improves your sleep quality at the same time. Yoga nidra is my personal savior when I feel burnout coming on. It is especially important because of that 'tired but wired' feeling that is so prevalent in burnout. When you are tired all damn day and then wired as soon as it's time to sleep, it's helpful to have a guide to send you into that relaxed space.

After all of this, if you still hate the idea of meditating: don't do it. I mean it. I am passionate about meditation and I know how powerful it can be, but if it is more stressful for you to meditate than it is to not meditate, you shouldn't be adding this one to your new routine.

I have seen the beginnings of meditation be especially difficult for those with previous trauma. If sitting quietly and breathing deeply triggers you, your best bet is to find a trauma-informed therapist who can work with you until you feel safe simply being in your body. I trust you to trust yourself. If meditation isn't a method that feels safe to you, it is truly okay for you to not do it.

Not wanting to meditate at all is something that comes up often in the one-on-one work I do online. Burnout is an extremely individual process even if some of the brain changes related to it are similar. Each person, mind, body and soul will react to burnout differently. It is important to recognize that there is no *right* way to recover from burnout, as long as you are doing something for yourself, you're doing a great job.

Sitting in The Muck

Not ready for meditation just yet, and not feeling the need for a therapist? Here's your way through emotions. I know we talked about sitting in the muck at the beginning of this book, but I want to be clear about what that means and exactly how you can do it. By giving you a method that allows you – nay, encourages you – to feel all the feels, my hope is that you give yourself permission to do the same. Your permission to go through this process is the most important part.

How to sit in the muck

Well, start by sitting in the muck. I mean it! When you feel an overpowering emotion, stop, sit down if you can, and allow yourself to *feel* this emotion on every level, mind, body and soul. This means not eating to avoid feeling. It means not Netflixing to avoid feeling. It means making space for this emotion without avoidance and without judgment. It also means learning to recognize what emotion you're feeling. This is harder than you might think. Most of us wave over emotions by saying things like "I'm stressed". But here's the thing about that – stress isn't an emotion. It's more likely that you're irritable, frustrated, or overwhelmed, all of which you could deal with head on if you were able to label and name these different aspects.

Here's an exercise to help you do this:

1. Stop. Sit down and agree to get interested in what it is like to actually feel the emotion that was triggered. Curiosity is the most important part of this process.

2. Look around the room. Find an object. Name and describe the object and where it is. (For example, grey pillow on the floor, red chair in the corner, blue vase on the shelf, old shelves on the wall, ugly lamp on the side table.) Do this until you feel a little calmer and slightly less distracted.

3. Now, feel inside your body. Name an emotion the same way that you named objects. (For instance, burning anger in my chest, heavy grief in my heart, big sadness on my shoulders.) Choose just one and do this as best you can. You'll get better with practice.

4. Once you've named the emotion, try describing. You don't have to do this perfectly. Here are some ideas. Does it have a color? Is it solid, liquid, or gas? Does it have a shape? If you chose burning anger in your chest, you might say it is "red and gas-like spreading and moving around, no particular shape but seems to seep into everything." Simply observe it and note your observations. It doesn't matter if you feel like you're making this up. It just matters that you put words to the sensations.

5. Then, answer the question: what would a five-year-old do to move this red gas like anger seeping into my body? And then answer the question with the first thing that comes to mind, even if it sounds silly. When I was writing this exercise, the thing that came into my mind was: vacuum it up.

6. Imagine yourself doing what a five-year-old would do to move the emotion.

7. Sit back and see how you feel.

8. Repeat as necessary.

Notice that this process doesn't ask you to unfeel the emotion or to ignore it. It asks you to *see* it and *feel* it and see if you can move it. If you're successful in moving all or part of it, that doesn't mean the emotion goes away forever. It just reminds you that the emotion is temporary and will change. Knowing this boosts your bouncebackability. If you're not 'successful', that simply becomes another thing that you notice. You can come back and try again.

You know you're ready to come out of the muck when you're able to do this with ease and it doesn't return. There's no judgment during this process. It's a place for curiosity and play. After a friend break-up, I rotated through anger, sadness, disappointment, and resentment for nearly two years before I was able to think about the situation without the emotions clouding it. At the time, I didn't wait that long to find silver linings, but I did allow myself that much time to process the situation. That person was important to me and losing them was painful. You aren't going to vacuum it up on a Wednesday when it happened on Tuesday and expect it to be gone.

The more you use this method, the more you get to know how particular emotions show up in your body and you'll start to recognize them better, again, building your bouncebackability. It's much easier to bounce back from something you see and recognize than from something unknown. For instance, if you feel anger often and you learn that anger often shows up in your particular body through a clenched jaw, you might start to recognize the jaw clench before you even feel the anger and be in a better position to do something about it. You'll become a master of emotional processing by understanding exactly how, when, and where physical emotional sensations appear in your body. Mastering just this one thing will dramatically change your life, decrease your burnout, and make you a happier human.

CHAPTER 21

FOCUS AND DEEP PRACTICE FOR RESOLVING BURNOUT

We've never before been at the mercy of such a barrage of information coming at us from every angle. Cell phones are the biggest distractors of our time. On top of these, we have copious messages being shoved at us every day. The different choices at grocery stores, the signs and billboards that hang in windows and line streets, the series waiting to be binged on Netflix. It just never ends.

This brings up two problems.

First, we are always distracted. When we are focused and then distracted, it takes 23 minutes to return to the task at hand. When was the last time you did anything for 23 minutes straight without checking your phone? We don't accomplish things to our skill level and we get less joy out of our accomplishments because it's hard to feel everything that went into a project when the time and energy spent was constantly disjointed.

Second, our brains never truly rest. Scrolling **isn't rest**. The emphasis was mostly for me, but maybe if I highlight it enough, you'll get this message loud and clear too. Up until the moment we drift off to sleep, we are ingesting information. Then, most of us aren't sleeping well enough to properly regenerate at night. Then, the inundation starts *as soon as our alarms go off* in the morning.

We don't even exercise without music or TV while on the treadmill at the gym. There's no quiet time. All of my best ideas have come out of quiet time. It's crucial to problem-solving and creativity.

So, how do you solve this?

You have to retrain yourself to focus. I started working on this about three years ago when I noticed that I couldn't read as long as I used to be able to without picking up my phone. I couldn't make it through a movie at home without picking up my phone. There's no way to really master a new skill or integrate new information that you've learned without repetition and practice and it's hard to get either of those when you're distracted.

The first step is to close down notifications. When I am writing, all my phone and computer notifications are off. In fact, most of the time my only phone notifications are calls and text. Everything else is shut off so that I'm not constantly beeping and interrupting myself.

The second step is to set a timer, and break work sessions into intervals. The Pomodoro technique is a popular way to do this. This technique was popularized in the 80s by Francisco Cirillo who used a tomato-shaped timer (thus the name 'pomodoro') to break up his time into 25-minute intervals while he was studying at university.

The 'original rules' for the Pomodoro technique are as follows:

Step 1: Decide on the task to be done.

Step 2: Set the Pomodoro timer (traditionally to 25 minutes). (I set a timer right in my web browser by typing the time into Google.)

Step 3: Work on the task.

Step 4: End work when the timer rings and put a checkmark on a piece of paper.

Step 5: If you have fewer than four checkmarks, take a short break of around 3 to 5 minutes, then go back to Step 2.

Step 6: After four Pomodoros, take a longer break of 15 to 30 minutes, reset your checkmark count to zero, then go back to Step 1.

The most important thing here is to work on the task the entire time without stopping to do anything else. It creates a sense of focus. When I started using this (I never did the checkmark part... just 25 minutes at a time followed by some stretching), I was amazed at how much I could get done in 20 to 25 minutes. If I was on a roll, I'd keep going, setting another timer before I continued. If I was losing steam or not finding words (I usually use this method for writing), I would either meditate or exercise – both are ways I like to use to clear my head and increase its malleability and thus creativity.

Because lack of accomplishment is such a big part of burnout, this is an incredible way to help yourself. Personally, it made me feel like a rockstar when I realized I could bang out a whole blog post in one 25-minute session and then do the social media for the blog post in the next 25 minutes. Before I started using this method, the same process took me about 3 hours... and I was so tired when I was done that it didn't feel celebratory or really all that impressive. Just the other day while I was writing, I noticed myself getting a little distracted. When I looked at the Baroque music on YouTube that I had started when I began writing, it was at 25 minutes. It made me laugh and reminded me... It's time for a break!

Movement

Physical activity has so many benefits. Asking someone to exercise when they are burnt out, however, is the wrong thing to do. When the body is begging for rest, she needs to get it. It was impossible for me to exercise when I was burnt out. I was so tired that I could barely walk up the hill to my house from the tram. It was a four-minute walk. That being said, it's still important. I'll bring you through all the reasons why and then give you a way to get moving that is doable for your current burnt-out body.

Physical movement does everything you need when it comes to building bouncebackability and avoiding burnout. In short, move your body, make your heart work, make your brain more malleable. Exercise can increase your brain's ability to change and grow, can increase your brain's resilience to stress, and makes you better able to learn. Sounds like a thing you need when you're burnt out, right?

The biggest benefits are found with exercising just three times per week either aerobic or strength training. Aerobic exercise includes anything that gets your heart rate up – cardio machines, walking, running, cross-country skiing (my fave!), cycling, dancing (my second fave!), aqua aerobics, boxing, hiking, etc. Strength training refers to resistance training using weights, but can be done simply using body weight as well.

If you want to start moving but you're fried crispy, try starting your day with a One Song Dance Party. You'll notice that I love using music as a support for veering away from burnout. One song at a time, you can breathe and dance your way out of most things.

Turn on one song that gets you going and dance like no one is watching. I promise, if nothing else, it will lift your mood. Doing just three minutes a day is better than doing nothing and is better than trying for a half-hour sweat session when your body isn't ready for that. So, get started with the smallest bit possible and work your way up when you're ready!

Do not, I repeat, *do not* go from a sedentary lifestyle straight to running a 5K. If you can't afford a trainer, start with a free app like Couch to 5K to get you from sedentary to moving again. While I'm a big exerciser, I've had a few years in my life where it fell to the wayside. The Couch to 5K program allowed me to get moving again without feeling like I was over-efforting. I've used it twice and liked it both times.

If you know the templates that work best for you, use them to decide on a plan. For instance, if you do better with accountability and other people, enlist a friend to exercise with you or join an exercise group near you. Meetups are a great place to find people that are looking to do what you are. If you don't find the group you want, start one! If you do great on your own but like someone in your ear, you can either get a trainer or download Aaptiv, a personal training app that won't break the bank.

When you have recovered, a regular exercise routine will help keep your bouncebackability stable and help you avoid burnout. But if you're a perfectionist and you've always exercised to an extreme, it's time to go back to getting honest with yourself and creating a routine that is *for you* not for fulfilling some crazy societal expectation that you believe people need from you. Over-exercising is just as bad as never moving at all!

Diet

Ugh, the dreaded dietary changes. I know, but hear me out. My qualifications allow me to discuss with you the dietary changes that are generally suggested in Chinese medicine. I like the set of rules in Chinese nutrition because I find them easy to apply and I notice that patients have good results with them. If, for whatever reason they don't suit you, find a nutritionist and get some help organizing a diet that suits your needs.

In Chinese medicine, burnout is related to the kidney and spleen energetic systems. This doesn't mean that something is wrong with your actual kidneys or spleen; it's simply the energetic system attached to the organ according to Chinese medicine. It is not in the scope of this book to delve deeply into Chinese nutritional theory, but there are great books out there if the following information interests you. I will be going over an extremely simplified version of the rules of eating according to Chinese medicine for the purposes of this book.

The simple rules are as follows:

1. Eat cooked, warm food. Raw food aficionados and smoothie lovers, I apologize. My medicine doesn't support your beliefs. I know there are studies that show raw food is helpful, especially after a cancer diagnosis and during treatment, and I'll say this: that makes sense in Chinese medicine. Chemotherapy and radiotherapy are both classified as *hot* therapies and therefore eating *cold* foods would be a good balance.

In everyday life, however, the Chinese theory is that warm food is easier for your body to digest, since some of the digestion is already done for you by way of heating. When you're burnt out and your body is tired, it's a good idea to make things as easy as possible for your body to handle. Soup, porridge, cooked veggies – all good options.

2. Eat foods that have strong colors. Spinach and kale, eggplant and black sesame seeds, any food that naturally has a strong color will be helpful for you. The theory is that you'll be able to transform your food into blood easier and you're supporting your kidney system at the same time.

3. Try to eat a balance of all five flavors: sweet, salty, bitter, sour, and spicy. Sweet here doesn't refer to candy and cake, but to foods like sweet potato or even rice. Salty doesn't mean potato chips but does refer to things like tuna, shrimp, and even black beans fall into this category. For bitter, things like arugula are a

good option. You'll find vinegar in the sour category and cayenne pepper in the spicy.

That's it. Well, not really. As I mentioned, there are multiple books and courses out there with All The Information, but if you're burnt out, stick with this list. Keep it simple.

Is this really that important? *Yes!* You might be tempted to not make any dietary changes, but I'm here to tell you that you should. Even if all you decide to do is cut out sugar, that's helpful. The gut bacteria, the body, the emotions, and the brain have this crazy relationship. Everything that happens in each of those systems affects the other systems. Long-term stress affects your brain, as we've talked about ad nauseum here, but did you know it also effs with your gut bacteria? Now you do!

Long-term stress increases the 'bad' bacteria in your gut and can lead to mood disorders. Now, if you've got a mixture of depression and burnout, or anxiety and burnout, or depression and anxiety and burnout, there's no getting through it without making your gut bacteria happier again. The easiest way to do that is good food. Fermented foods, real foods, seriously cutting down on sugar – all great ways to help that microbiome thrive in a way that will support everything else that you're doing.

It's worth it, I promise. If you want to see some crazy research on diets healing depression and other mental illnesses, check out Kelly Brogan, M.D.'s book *A Mind of Your Own*. It'll make you see the entire world in a whole new light.

Media Diet

I am a self-professed Facebook lover and Instagram is my mistress. I scroll and scroll. I love the ability it gave me to stay close to my family even when I was far away.

But...

Winter 2017 found my husband and me in northern Finland with cross-country skis, wooden huts, outhouses, no electrical sockets, and certainly no internet. We covered 120 kms in six days, carrying all our luggage with us on a sled that was attached to one set of hips or the other throughout the week.

Before this trip, I was excited about the prospect of being free of social media and phone for a week, I knew it would be helpful, but I had no idea how much. My mind was clearer than it had been in *years*. I know that large amounts of exercise and fresh air added to my clarity, but I cannot minimize the effect of no social media.

I'll be honest... I wasn't happy every day I was there, but I still wasn't reaching for my phone. I didn't even want to, and I am absolutely, without a doubt, addicted. Instead of reaching for my phone, for that one week, I sat with my emotions. I dealt with the fact that day two was -25 Celsius with 50 kph winds and I couldn't see where the eff I was going. I went through a rollercoaster of irritation, frustration, exhaustion, awe, gratitude, expansion. That trip changed my mind about phone time and when I got back... I went straight back to normal. Maybe it took a week, but I was sucked back in like a junkie.

It wasn't until my Croatian writing retreat for this book in September 2018 that I gave myself another respite. Two days. Just two simple days. Admittedly, I spent less time on social media naturally when I was writing because I was focused, but I did use it to give myself a break, the way smokers use cigarettes – a little treat for writing for 25 or 45 minutes. *Good job, Caity. Here's some Facebook distraction.*

Here's the thing about that. *There's no rest for the Facebook-addicted among us.* If you're tired, not sleeping well, unable to rest in a way that is regenerating, *put down your damn phone.*

Social media, like TV, is designed to play on your emotions. I don't care how relaxing you think a Netflix binge is, it's not. It does not give your mind the space it needs to recoup from your day. It keeps you highly stimulated, at least on a brain level, and creates all sorts of bodily reactions that you have no business having.

How do I know this? Mirror neurons. Mirror neurons in your brain ensure that when you see someone stub their toe, you cringe too. Your body and brain react to it as if it happened to you. We've gone over filters enough by now for you to understand: if you're reacting (and you are) internally to what's happening with 'your' characters on 'your' TV show, all that shit is *happening to you too*. The more you repeat and repeat that, the more your brain will look for evidence of it in your actual life. It's art imitating life imitating art. Talk about heightened drama. It's no surprise that we are hooked into certain shows. They hit us where it hurts and we keep going back for more.

If you want to avoid burnout, you'll have to create social media, TV, and news (*yes, news!*) boundaries. I'll leave you with books, because you have to do something and the action is slower, generally, than TV. So you experience things, yes, but to a lesser extent because reading for an hour hardly gets you the same input as an hour of TV.

Here's some interesting math to spike your desire to shift. If you spend two hours a day on social media (almost everyone I know manages this, especially if you have an online business), you're spending, at the end of the year a total of *one entire month* on social media. Here, I'll show you:

2 hours x 365 days = 730 hours

730 hours / 24 hours per day = 30.42 days =

1 month of your year going to social media

If we break that down into just eight hours a day because no one is saying you should be productive every hour of the day, it turns into three months of working days wasted on social media. Three effing months. And you complain that you don't have enough time.

Add one hour of the news and an hour of TV and now you've spent two months out of twelve (or six months at an eight-hour a day schedule) fully immersed in shit that doesn't matter.

In order to give a shit about things that matter again, you need to eliminate things that don't. We're coming back around to honesty. If you aren't sure how much time you're spending on your phone, there are apps for that. Thrive Global has an app for this exact purpose. Go ahead, turn them on, find out just how much time you are scrolling for that dopamine rush instead of living the life you actually want to live.

In honor of total honesty, as I write this, I'm beginning a two-day writing session for my book. Just before I started, I deleted Facebook and IG from my phone so I could have two social-media-free days before I head back to the real world. I also used an extension for Google Chrome called Focused to shut down access to Facebook and IG on my computer while I write. It's been 30 minutes. I'm already itching. In a few hours, it will be over, but if you scratch the itch, 45 minutes goes by and you have no idea how. Stop scratching the itch.

CHAPTER 22

WHEN MEDICAL INTERVENTION IS NECESSARY

It is common in my field to have disdain for medical doctors. Sure, there are some things that frustrate me about the medical system and Big Pharma, but generally, I have more of a desire to coexist peacefully, and more importantly, put our patients in front of our egos.

I've already covered in depth that there are physiological changes that happen with burnout and I want to reiterate that here to remind you that sometimes medical intervention is necessary. Now that the World Health Organization has started recognizing burnout as a thing, maybe doctors will pay a little more attention and take it more seriously.

The intervention that is recommended might be anything from iron supplements to antidepressants, and if you need them, you should take them. I know plenty of women who have done a course of antidepressants just to be able to do the further inner work that is required. I have heard *too many* women say, "I wish I had done this sooner" and it breaks my heart that they waited to get the help they needed because they were judging themselves for taking a pill.

I also believe that a great psychotherapist is often necessary during burnout. I know this book is great, but it may not solve all your problems! (wink emoji) If what this book does is convince you to take care of yourself in the best way possible *for you* right now, then my work here is done.

I do implore you, however, to have a full physical done with a full blood panel. If you find out you're anemic or have a thyroid condition – those are things that need to be treated* and can help you eliminate some of the guilt, blame and shame you carry around. There *really is* something wrong!

Now, you still need to do the rest of the work. Your body doesn't react like this for no reason. However, you can choose to do the work while medicated and make it easier on yourself if that's what you need.

If you do all of the necessary tests and your regular MD doesn't notice anything alarming, but you're still convinced something is off that could be corrected with a specific diet or a supplement, I'd recommend that you see someone who practices functional medicine. Functional medicine uses in-depth lab testing of blood, urine, stool, or saliva to discover underlying causes of health issues and develop individualized treatment plans to achieve what they refer to as 'optimal health'. Following lab testing, there will be dietary and supplement recommendations for you to follow. It has been crucial for me and many of my patients in getting well. I implore you to use this route instead of asking the girl who works at Whole Foods to tell you what supplement to take.

The difference between conventional medicine and lab work and functional medicine and lab work is specificity. For instance, recently I was at the doctor and I know that I have high thyroid antibodies. This is a test that would be important in functional medicine because they want to know everything, have the whole picture and aim for optimal health in all areas. My conventional doctor told me that this test was unnecessary and means nothing if my thyroid hormone levels are normal. So, even though I know that something is going wrong in my body, conventional medicine says it's unimportant (mostly because they don't know what to do with the information), while functional medicine might suggest increasing omega threes and excluding gluten – both ways to decrease the number of antibodies to my thyroid and thus decrease the attack on my thyroid.

Nothing works for everyone. Get specific about what you'll take, and you'll get further faster and spend less money in the long run! Often, functional medicine doctors also practice Chinese Medicine. If you can find a combo like that, you've won the jackpot.

*I healed my own thyroid with Chinese medicine, the tools in this book, and a functional medicine practitioner.

CHAPTER 23

FIRST SAVE YOURSELF

Avoiding burnout is not always fun, but it is always doable. It's full of making choices that go against the habits and systems of your brain that were created and designed to make things easier. It's full of uncomfortable moments and learning to sit in the muck without spiritually bypassing. It's showing up for yourself in a world that offers you so many possible outlets for distraction. It's being honest about what things in your internal and external environments aren't working for you. It's about letting go of the templates that you downloaded as a child and creating some that are a better match for you. It's about building a business and life you love most of the time (nothing is perfect all the time) that energizes you and sustains you mentally, emotionally, physically, and spiritually.

My dream for you after you finish this book is that you will feel understood, validated, and empowered to take inspired action to break away from burnout. My vision for female entrepreneurs in the (very near!) future is that we will build the businesses that change the world. We will bring forth kindness, understanding, and service, all while making money and tending to our own needs. We will teach our friends, sisters, mothers, aunts, and daughters that the new way is here now, that sacrificing ourselves 'for the greater good' is no longer on the menu.

I see you feeling more grounded and solid in your decision-making powers, making choices that are in alignment with your inner world instead of to other people's expectations. I see you noticing roadblocks ahead and turning back to this book for guidance and tools on how to get through it (or avoid it altogether). I can already *feel* the shift happening. The more of us who read this book and talk about our experiences, the more healing that will happen. Just by being here and reading this book for yourself, you've become part of a movement to #endburnoutculture, and I am so proud to walk beside you.

The Dalai Lama once said that Western woman would save the world. I think we have a strong chance of doing this in our lifetimes if we can focus first on saving ourselves. Ending burnout is creating liberation for the generations both before us and after us.

Thank you for coming on this journey. I honor and appreciate your time and your story more than you know. Hearing your stories is one of my favorite things, so please don't hesitate to write to me if you feel called. We're all in this together, we're all connected, and we'll get through it as a team.

Sending you love and magic,

Cait

P.S. Part of being bouncebackable is having a supportive community to share your journey with. To that end, I created a Facebook group for readers and fans of The Bouncebackability Factor to connect and continue the conversation. A major lesson that I learned throughout my healing is this: sometimes, we need people outside of us to show us how to love ourselves, trust ourselves, prioritize ourselves. I know that the personal development world would have you believe that you can go off and 'fix' all your shit by focusing on the positive and only attracting goodness. But I tried that for years and it wasn't until I allowed myself to be loved unconditionally from the outside that I truly started loving myself from the inside.

I want you to come join us, to join a community of women who will support, love, and prioritize you in order to help you grow those abilities in yourself. We are waiting to welcome you with open arms. You'll find us here: https://www.facebook.com/groups/bouncebackability

P.P.S. Yes, I do work 1:1 with clients! We always begin with a complimentary consult to be sure we are a good fit and that this is what you need. You can book a call by going to: bit.ly/callcait

P.P.P.S. I'm sticking around now because I don't want to leave you! Come find me on Instagram, post a picture of your favorite passage from the book, and tag me in it! @cait_donovan

ABOUT THE AUTHOR

Caitlin Donovan is one of NYC's leading burnout experts, acupuncturist, and host of FRIED – The Burnout Podcast. With a Master's degree in Traditional Chinese Medicine, Caitlin combines Eastern wisdom with her natural practicality. After over 25,000 patient visits, Caitlin pivoted into 1:1 coaching and DIY courses, corporate workshops, and keynotes with companies such as PTC and Lululemon – all with a focus on burnout.

She has been featured on podcasts and online magazines such as Elephant Journal, Thrive Global, Addicted 2 Success, The Confidence Academy, and Your Story Your Health.

Caitlin and her husband spent 12 years living in Europe and now have made their home in NJ with Flora, their white fluffy dog. When Caitlin is not speaking or coaching on burnout, you can count on finding her hiking, golfing, or cross-country skiing.

ACKNOWLEDGMENTS

I could fill an entire second book with thank yous and head nods to all the people that have had to exist to bring me to the place where this book was created. It would include everyone I've ever met and every author I've ever read. I'll start at the beginning and make a sincere attempt to be precise.

My parents – for raising me to believe that I can trust my decisions and follow my heart. Without them, none of this adventure would have been possible.

My husband, Marcin – for proposing after knowing me for six short weeks and getting on board when I say it's time to move countries. Also, for coining the term Mother effin' Teresa syndrome.

My sister – for her unwavering faith that there's something special about me, even when I'm in sincere doubt of that myself. Your faith feeds my own.

My bestie, Ewa – as my best friend, the person who taught me to be a coach, and the person who taught me that I was worthy of unconditional love. My burnout healing would have never happened without you.

To my clients and patients – there is no group of people that taught me more than you. Your stories mirrored my own. We heal together. I am so blessed to work and to have worked with you. Thank you.

To every single contributor to the campaign to get this book published and Lindsey Garant, owner of La Lune Healing, who created rewards that flew off the shelves and helped me get there.

Especially to Agnieszka Servaas whose generous donation means that this book will be published in two languages. Your belief in me brings me to tears and I am so lucky to have you in my life.

To BSchoolers – you know who you are. Without the support of my fellow Bs, there is no way I would have honed my message and found the gold of what I truly wanted to write. Being inspired by you every day helped keep me on track and led me to: Kris Emery, my editor. Editor extraordinaire. Every single suggestion you made improved this book. It would not have reached its potential without you. And Annick Ina, my book doula and first reader. Without your feedback, this may have ended up stuck on my computer for years to come. Thank you for believing in me.

Lastly, to all the women who were caught on the burnout cycle before I was – for your stories, emotions, experiences, and lives. Our collective consciousness finally banded. It's time to #endburnoutculture for good!

WORKS CITED

Alini, E. (2017, August 2). *'Burnout' is a thing, doctors, say. Here are the symptoms.* Retrieved from Global News: https://globalnews.ca/news/3639388/burnout-syndrome-symptoms-stress/

Aron, E. (2012). *The Highly Senstive Person: How to Thrive When the World Overwhlems You.* HarperCollins.

Bourg Carter, S. D. (2010). *High Octane Women.* Prometheus Books.

Christina Maslach, P. G. (1982). *Burnout: The Cost of Caring.* Englewood Cliffs: Prentice-Hall.

Glouberman, D. (2007). *The Joy Of Burnout: How the end of the world can be a new beginning.* Skyros Books.

Maslach, C., Lee, K., & Neason, A. (2018, August 20). Burnout. (M. (. Moss-Coane, Interviewer)

McEwan, B. (2017, April 10). *Pub Med.* Retrieved from NCBI: https://www.ncbi.nlm.nih.gov/pubmed/28856337

Patz, A. (2015, November 5). Retrieved from Prevention: https://www.prevention.com/life/a20486040/depression-or-burnout/

Ropeik, D. (2012, March 23). *Chronic Stress Can Shrink Your Brain.* Retrieved from Psychology Today: https://www.psychologytoday.com/us/blog/how-risky-is-it-really/201203/chronic-stress-can-shrink-your-brain

van der Kolk, B. (2014). *The Body Keeps The Score; Brain, Mind, and Body in teh Healing of Trauma.* Viking.

Wellwood, J. (2011). Human Nature, Buddha Nature: On Spiritual Bypassing, Relationship, adn the Dharma. (T. Fossella, Interviewer)

RESOURCES

FOR TRAUMA

The Transformation: Discovering Wholeness and Healing After Trauma, Dr. James Gordon
Healing Racial Trauma: The Road to Resilience and The Well of Life, Sheila Wise Rowe
Patriarchy Stress Disorder: The Invisible Barrier to Women's Happiness and Fulfillment, Dr. Valerie Rein
INSTAGRAM ACCOUNTS:
@brittfrank (Psychotherapist and trauma specialist – Britt Frank)
@sitwithwhit (Psychotherapist – Whitney Goodman)
@blacktraumamatters (Psychologist – Dr. Samara Touissant)

FOR HEART RATE VARIABILITY

The Heart Math Institute – https://www.heartmath.com
Oura Right – https://www.ouraring.com

FOR SUICIDE SUPPORT

Suicide Help – https://www.suicidepreventionhotline.org

FOR NUTRITION SUPPORT

INSTAGRAM ACCOUNTS
@foodheaven
@carolynbrownie
@isabelsmithnutrition

FOR FUNCTIONAL MEDICINCE

Mel Hopper Koppelman,
https://www.harborintegrativehealth.com/
Caitlin Gordon, https://amalunawellness.com/

FOR CHINESE MEDICINE / ACUPUNCTURE

This needs to be local, for obvious reasons! I will be happy to help you find someone close to you, just reach out at cait@caitdonovan.com

FOR ANTI-HUSTLE CULTURE

Chillpreneur: The New Rules for Creating Success, Freedom, and Abundance on Your Terms, Denise Duffield Thomas
Do Less: A Revolutionary Approach to Time and Energy Management for Ambitious Women, Kate Northrup
Profit First: Transform Your Business from a Cash-Eating Monster to a Money-Making Machine, Mike Michalowicz

FOR SPIRITUALITY

Outrageous Openness: Letting The Divine Take the Lead, Tosha Silver
Soul Care in African American Practice, Barbara Peacock

FOR BOUNDARIES

Setting Boundaries Will Set You Free: The Ultimate Guide to Telling the Truth, Creating Connection, and Finding Freedom, Nancy Levin

FOR SLEEP

The Sleep Revolution: Transforming Your Life, One Night at a Time, Arianna Huffington
Rewired for Sleep: The 28 Day Insomnia Repair Program, Daniel R. Bernstein

OTHER BURNOUT RESOURCES

Burnout: The Secret to Unlocking the Stress Cycle, Emily and Amelia Nagoski
Life in 4 Part Harmony, Dr. Sandra Lewis

Made in the USA
Las Vegas, NV
11 September 2021